Super Skills for Summer Practice

I Did It!

Alphabet

Big and Little

Draw a line to make a match.

See the capital **A**.

See the lowercase **a**.

I Can Write

Trace and write the letters.

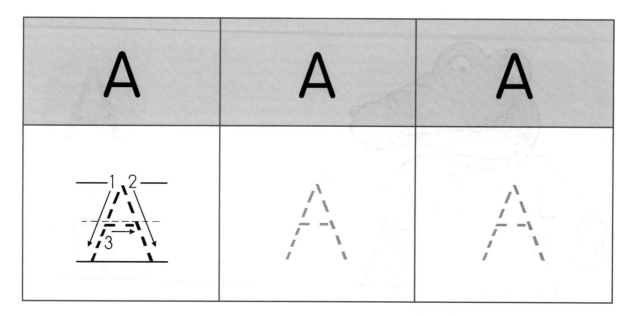

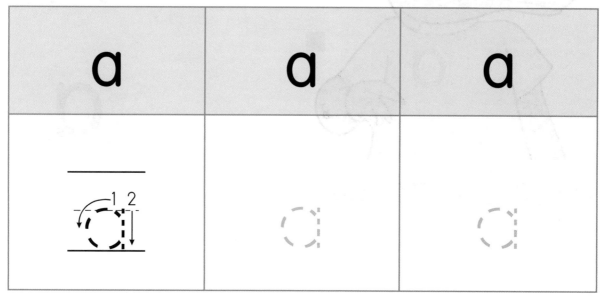

Super Skills for Summer • EMC 9830 • © Evan-Moor Corp.

Find It

Circle the letters that are the same as the first letter.

A	N	A	A	B
a	b	a	n	a

Find the big **A** and the little **a**. Circle them.

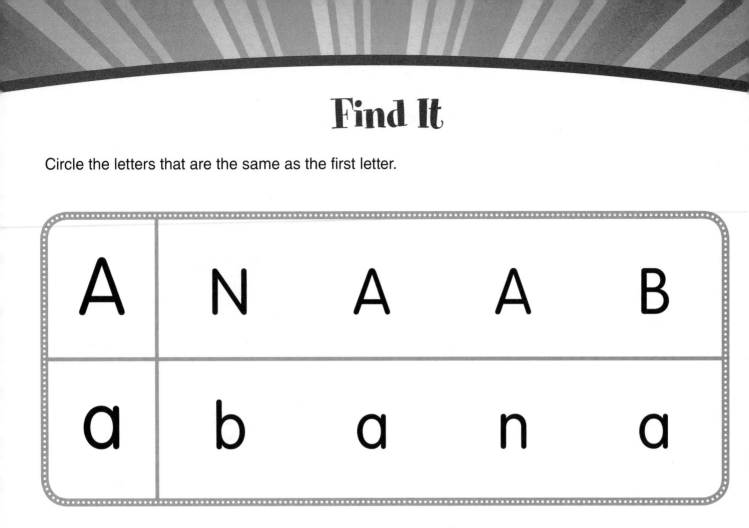

A B C D E F G H I J K L M
N O P Q R S T U V W X Y Z

a b c d e f g h i j k l m
n o p q r s t u v w x y z

Same Sound

Name the picture.
Color it if it begins with the same sound as *ant*.

Big and Little

Draw a line to make a match.

See the capital **B**.

See the lowercase **b**.

I Can Write

Trace and write the letters.

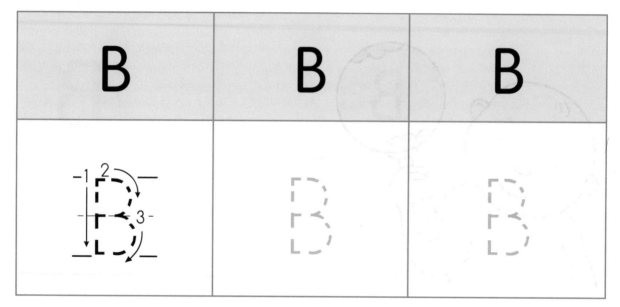

B	B	B

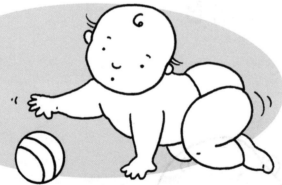

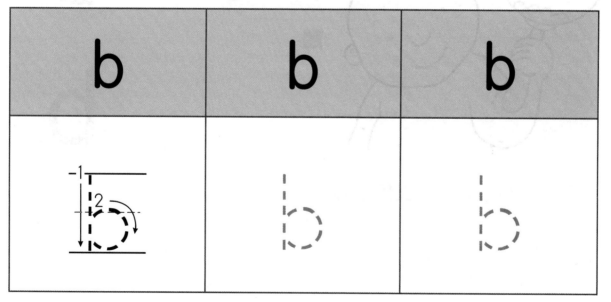

b	b	b

Find It

Circle the letters that are the same as the first letter.

B	L B A B
b	b r n b

Find the big **B** and the little **b**. Circle them.

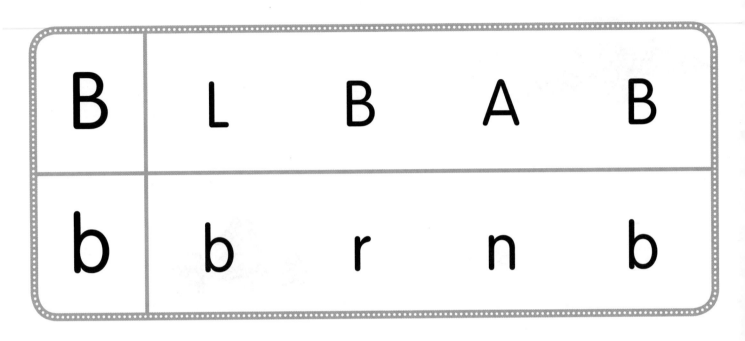

A B C D E F G H I J K L M
N O P Q R S T U V W X Y Z

a b c d e f g h i j k l m
n o p q r s t u v w x y z

Fly Away Home

Trace the bat's path to his cave.

Trace the letters.

Same Sound

Name the picture.
Color it if it begins with the same sound as *bear*.

Big and Little

Draw a line to make a match.

See the capital **C**.

See the lowercase **c**.

I Can Write

Trace and write the letters.

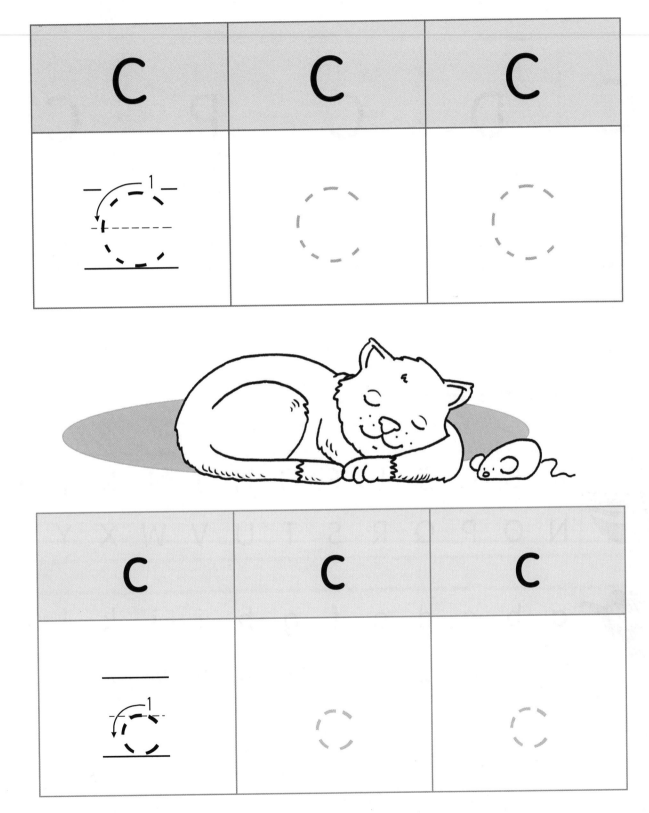

Find It

Circle the letters that are the same as the first letter.

C	D	C	P	C
c	p	c	c	d

Find the big **C** and the little **c**. Circle them.

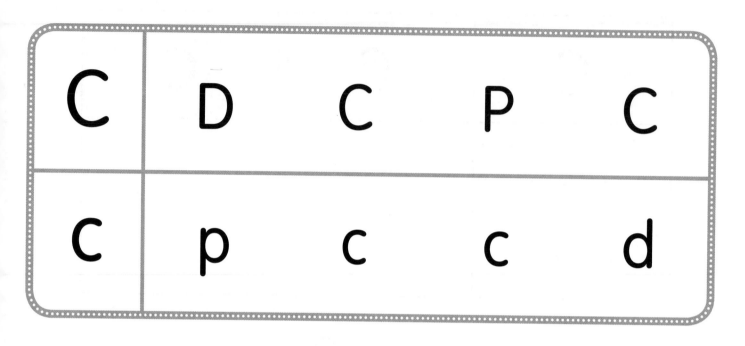

A B C D E F G H I J K L M
N O P Q R S T U V W X Y Z

a b c d e f g h i j k l m
n o p q r s t u v w x y z

Cat Fun

Connect the dots.

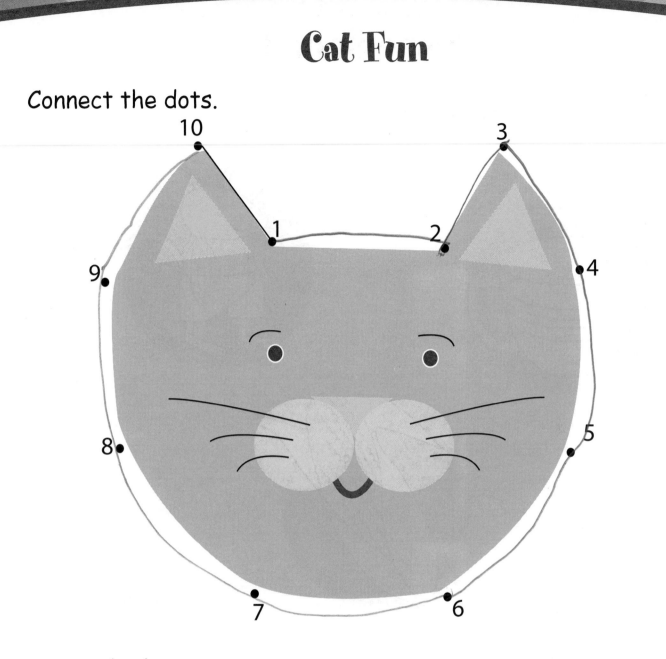

Trace the letters.

Same Sound

Name the picture.
Color it if it begins with the same sound as *cat*.

Super Skills for Summer • EMC 9830 • © Evan-Moor Corp.

Big and Little

Draw a line to make a match.

See the capital **D**.

See the lowercase **d**.

I Can Write

Trace and write the letters.

D	D	D
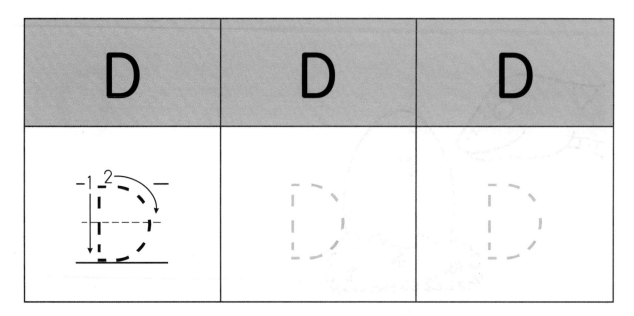		

d	d	d
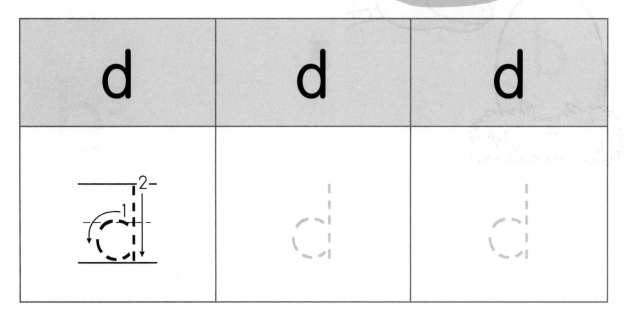		

Find It

Circle the letters that are the same as the first letter.

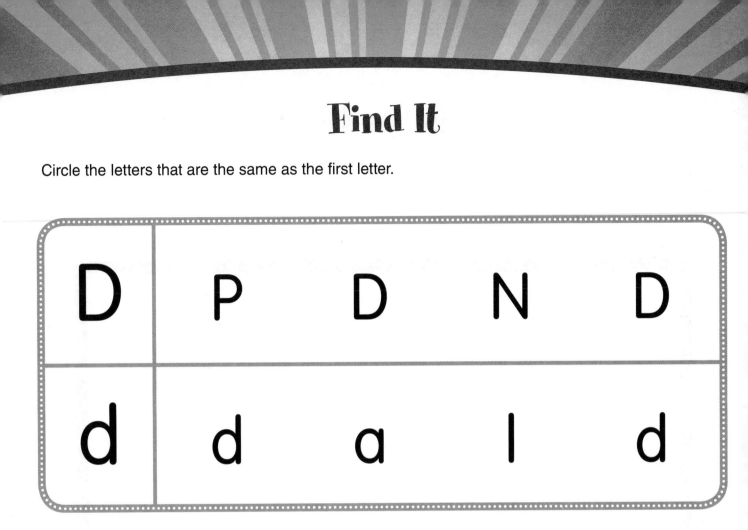

D	P	D	N	D
d	d	a	l	d

Find the big **D** and the little **d**. Circle them.

A B C D E F G H I J K L M
N O P Q R S T U V W X Y Z

a b c d e f g h i j k l m
n o p q r s t u v w x y z

D Is for Duck

Trace the duck.
Color the duck.

Trace the letters.

Same Sound

Name the picture.
Color it if it begins with the same sound as **dog**.

Big and Little

Draw a line to make a match.

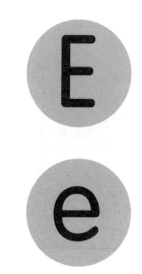

See the capital **E**.

See the lowercase **e**.

I Can Write

Trace and write the letters.

Find It

Circle the letters that are the same as the first letter.

E	L	E	E	B
e	e	a	e	o

Find the big **E** and the little **e**. Circle them.

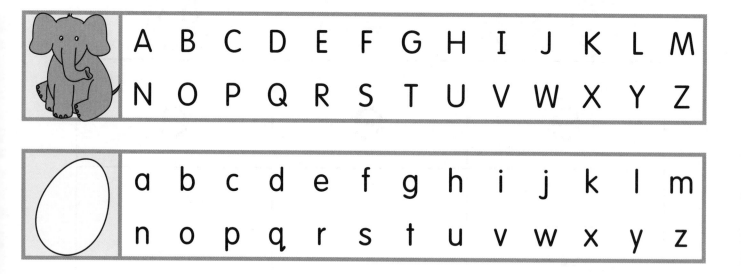

A B C D E F G H I J K L M
N O P Q R S T U V W X Y Z

a b c d e f g h i j k l m
n o p q r s t u v w x y z

Same Sound

Name the picture.
Color it if it begins with the same sound as **elephant**.

Big and Little

Draw a line to make a match.

See the capital **F**.

 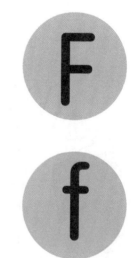

See the lowercase **f**.

Super Skills for Summer • EMC 9830 • © Evan-Moor Corp.

I Can Write

Trace and write the letters.

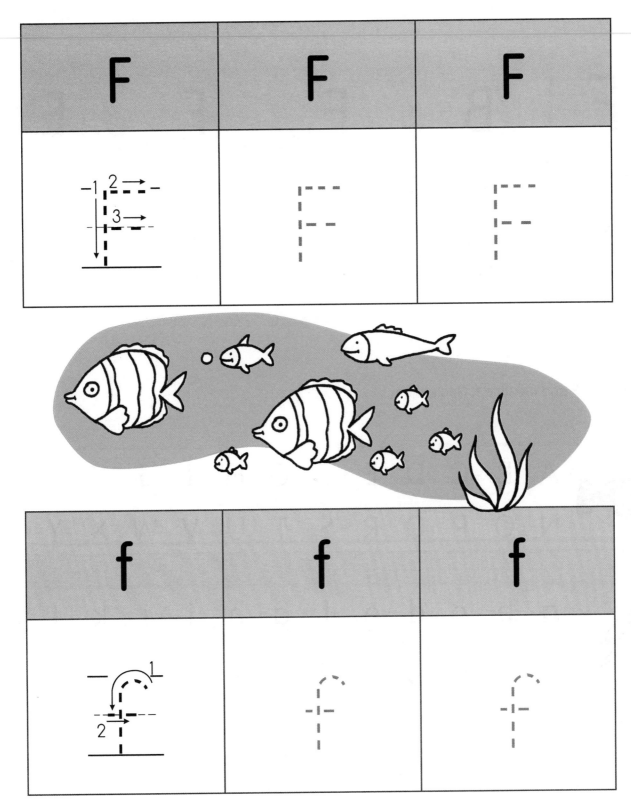

Find It

Circle the letters that are the same as the first letter.

F	B	F	F	E
f	d	l	f	f

Find the big **F** and the little **f**. Circle them.

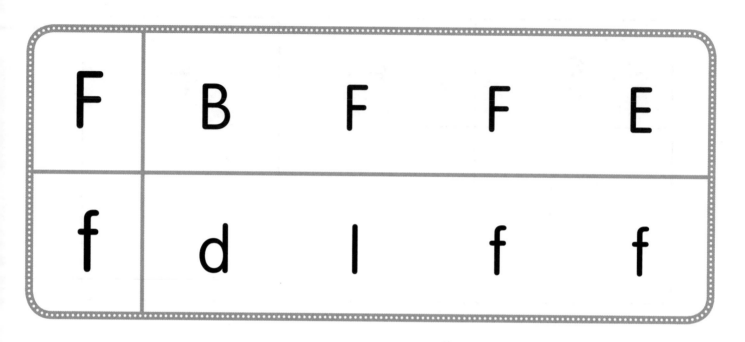

A B C D E F G H I J K L M
N O P Q R S T U V W X Y Z

a b c d e f g h i j k l m
n o p q r s t u v w x y z

Super Skills for Summer • EMC 9830 • © Evan-Moor Corp.

Funny Fish

Color the pictures that begin like **fish**.

Trace the letters.

Same Sound

Name the picture.
Color it if it begins with the same sound as *fish*.

Big and Little

Draw a line to make a match.

See the capital **G**.

See the lowercase **g**.

I Can Write

Trace and write the letters.

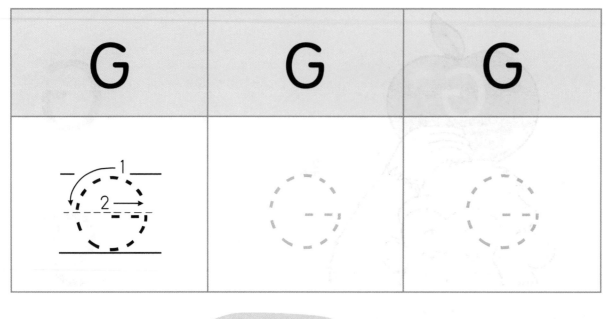

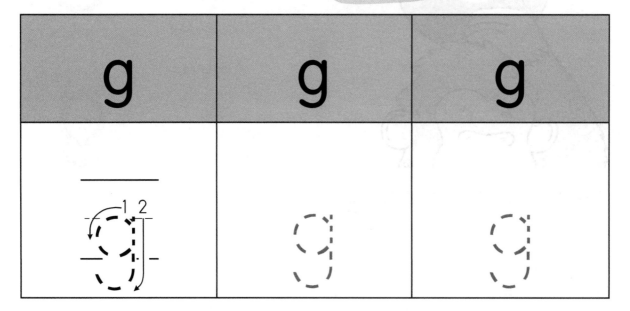

Super Skills for Summer • EMC 9830 • © Evan-Moor Corp.

Find It

Circle the letters that are the same as the first letter.

G	G	O	D	G
g	f	g	b	g

Find the big **G** and the little **g**. Circle them.

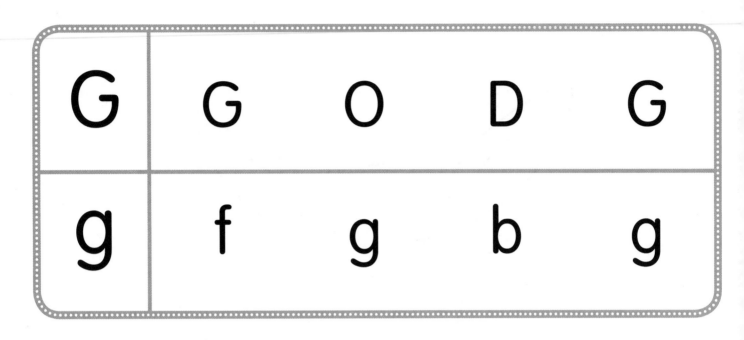

A B C D E F G H I J K L M
N O P Q R S T U V W X Y Z

a b c d e f g h i j k l m
n o p q r s t u v w x y z

Listen for the Sound

Trace the horns.
Color the goat.

See the goat.

They all start like **goat**.

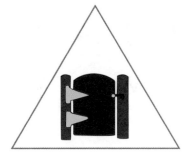  

Same Sound

Name the picture.
Color it if it begins with the same sound as *gorilla*.

Big and Little

Draw a line to make a match.

See the capital **H**.

See the lowercase **h**.

I Can Write

Trace and write the letters.

Find It

Circle the letters that are the same as the first letter.

H	A	H	H	N
h	b	h	n	h

Find the big **H** and the little **h**. Circle them.

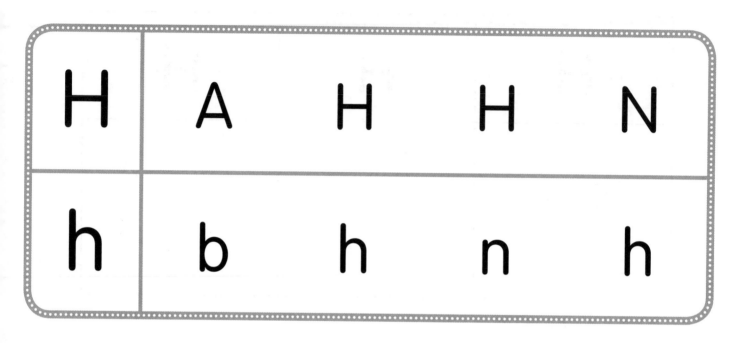

A B C D E F G H I J K L M
N O P Q R S T U V W X Y Z

a b c d e f g h i j k l m
n o p q r s t u v w x y z

Same or Different?

Circle the pictures in each row that are the same.

Trace the letters.

Same Sound

Name the picture.
Color it if it begins with the same sound as *hen*.

Big and Little

Draw a line to make a match.

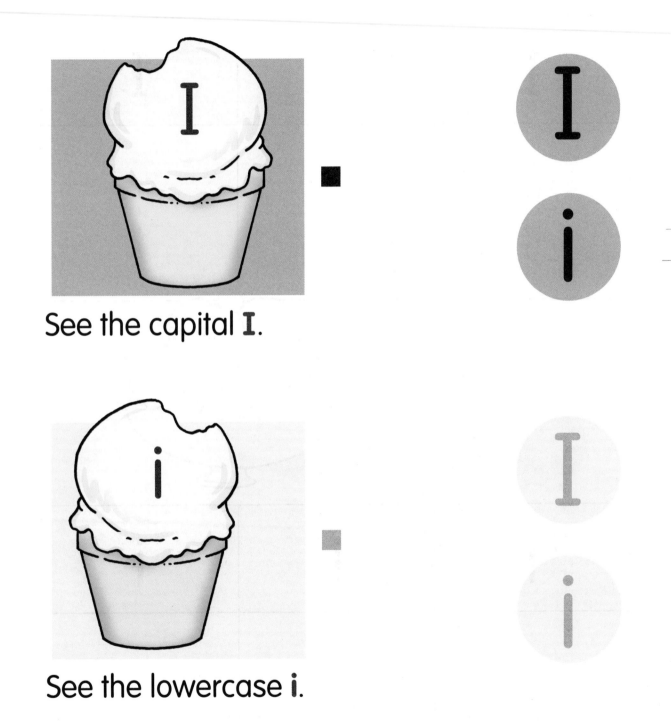

See the capital **I**.

See the lowercase **i**.

I Can Write

Trace and write the letters.

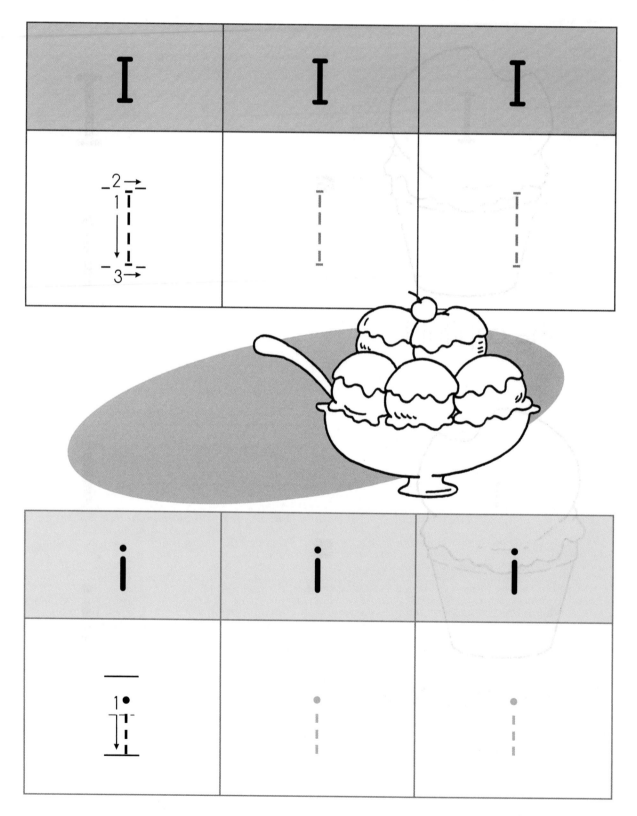

Super Skills for Summer • EMC 9830 • © Evan-Moor Corp.

Find It

Circle the letters that are the same as the first letter.

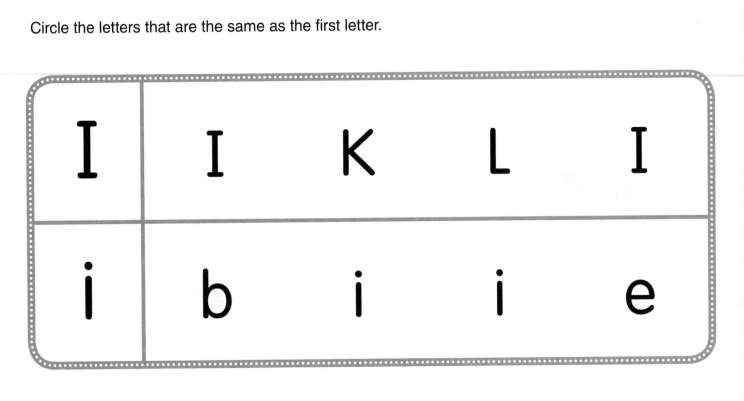

I	I	K	L	I
i	b	i	i	e

Find the big **I** and the little **i**. Circle them.

A B C D E F G H I J K L M
N O P Q R S T U V W X Y Z

a b c d e f g h i j k l m
n o p q r s t u v w x y z

Same Sound

Name the picture.
Color it if it begins with the same sound as *iguana*.

Big and Little

Draw a line to make a match.

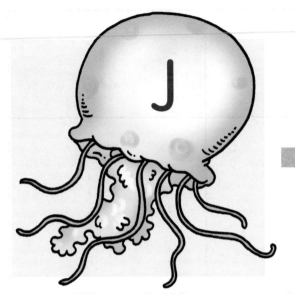

See the capital **J**.

J

j

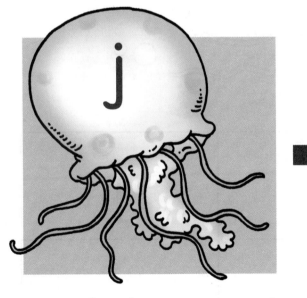

See the lowercase **j**.

J

j

I Can Write

Trace and write the letters.

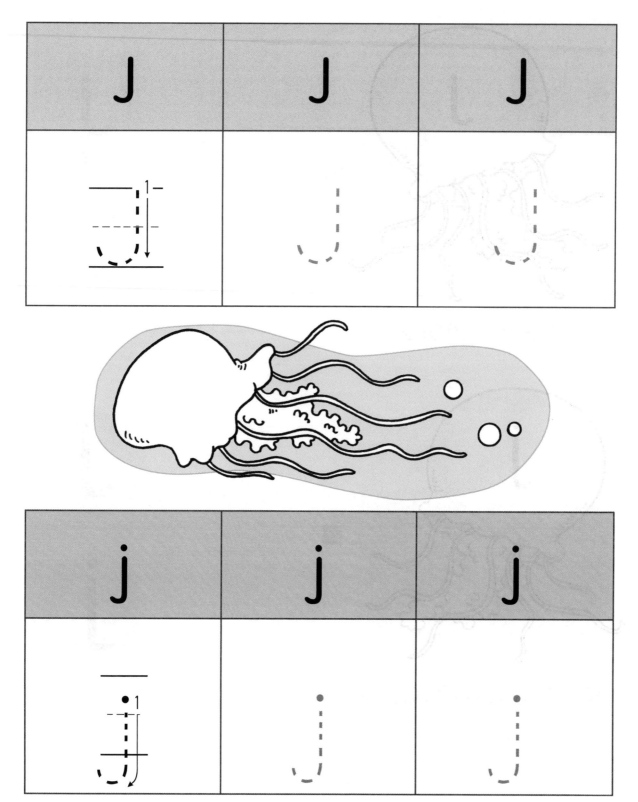

Super Skills for Summer • EMC 9830 • © Evan-Moor Corp.

Find It

Circle the letters that are the same as the first letter.

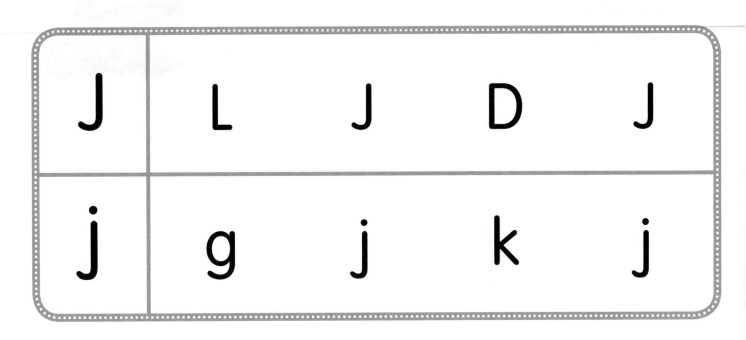

J	L	J	D	J
j	g	j	k	j

Find the big **J** and the little **j**. Circle them.

A B C D E F G H I J K L M
N O P Q R S T U V W X Y Z

a b c d e f g h i j k l m
n o p q r s t u v w x y z

Finish the Jet

Draw what is missing.
Color the jet to match.

Trace the letters.

J J J J j j j j

Same Sound

Name the picture.
Color it if it begins with the same sound as *jaguar*.

Big and Little

Draw a line to make a match.

See the capital **K**.

See the lowercase **k**.

 Super Skills for Summer • EMC 9830 • © Evan-Moor Corp.

I Can Write

Trace and write the letters.

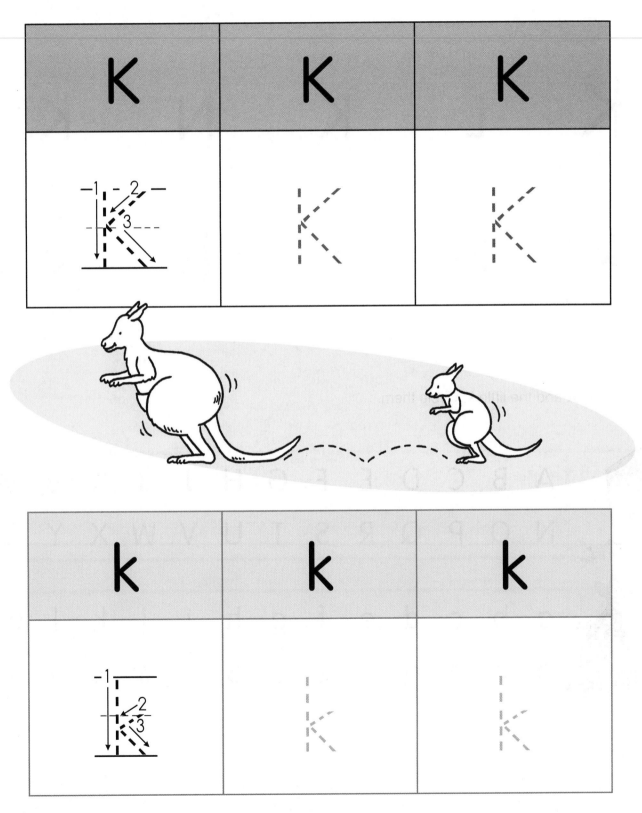

Find It

Circle the letters that are the same as the first letter.

K	L	K	N	K
k	k	i	h	k

Find the big **K** and the little **k**. Circle them.

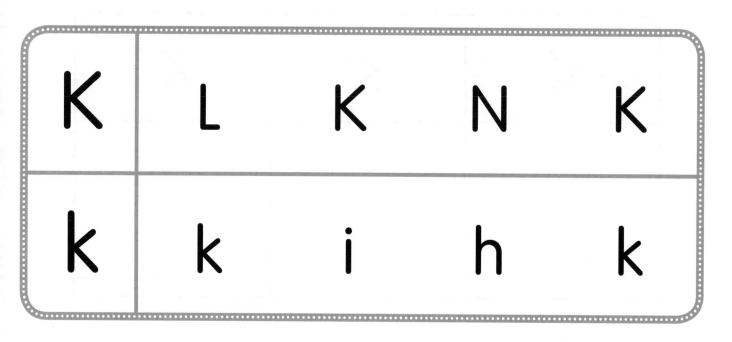

A B C D E F G H I J K L M
N O P Q R S T U V W X Y Z

a b c d e f g h i j k l m
n o p q r s t u v w x y z

Kangaroos Hop

Trace.

Trace the letters.

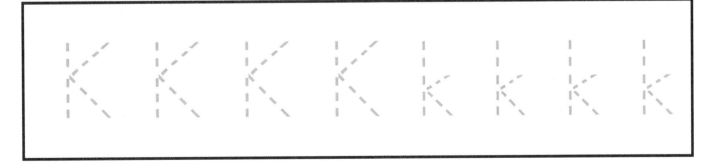

Same Sound

Name the picture.
Color it if it begins with the same sound as *koala*.

Big and Little

Draw a line to make a match.

See the capital **L**.

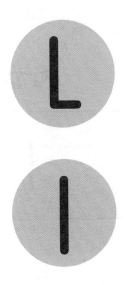

See the lowercase **l**.

I Can Write

Trace and write the letters.

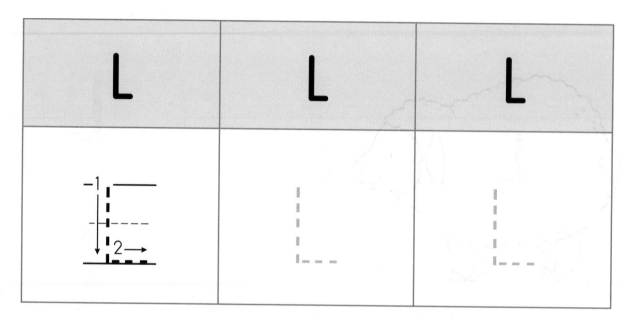

L	L	L

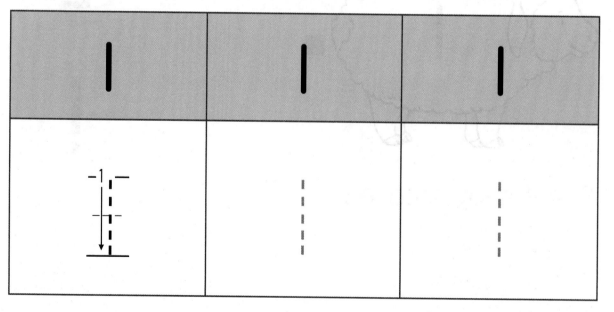

I	I	I

Find It

Circle the letters that are the same as the first letter.

L	L	L	G	H
l	d	l	l	i

Find the big **L** and the little **l**. Circle them.

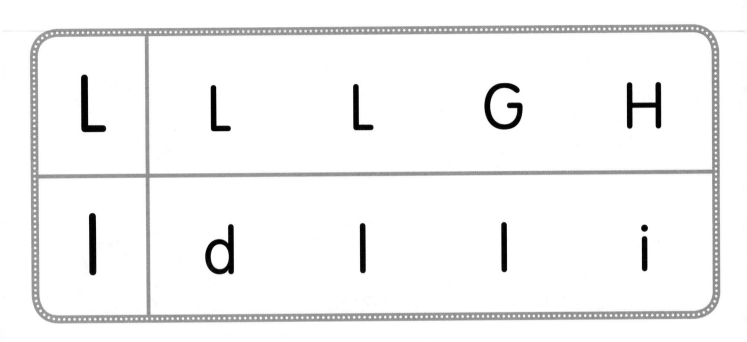

A B C D E F G H I J K L M
N O P Q R S T U V W X Y Z

a b c d e f g h i j k l m
n o p q r s t u v w x y z

Same or Different?

Circle the pictures in each row that are the same.

Trace the letters.

Same Sound

Name the picture.
Color it if it begins with the same sound as *lamb*.

Big and Little

Draw a line to make a match.

See the capital **M**.

See the lowercase **m**.

Super Skills for Summer • EMC 9830 • © Evan-Moor Corp.

I Can Write

Trace and write the letters.

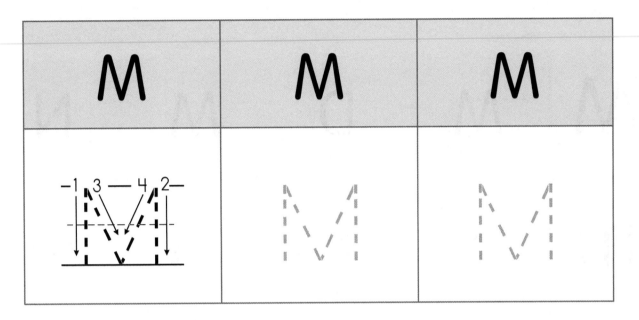

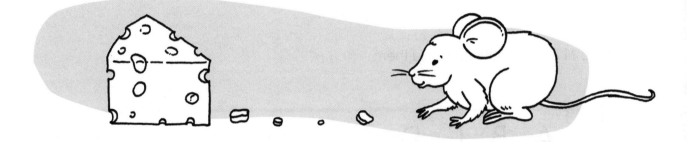

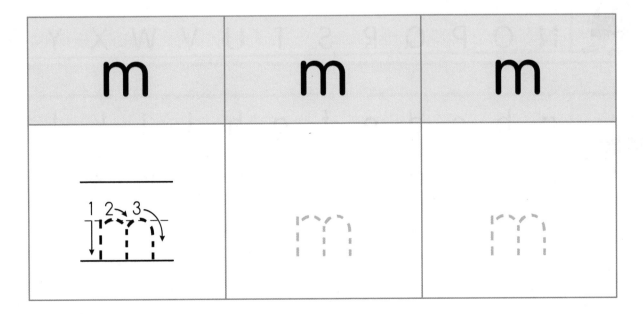

Find It

Circle the letters that are the same as the first letter.

M	M	D	M	N
m	r	p	m	m

Find the big **M** and the little **m**. Circle them.

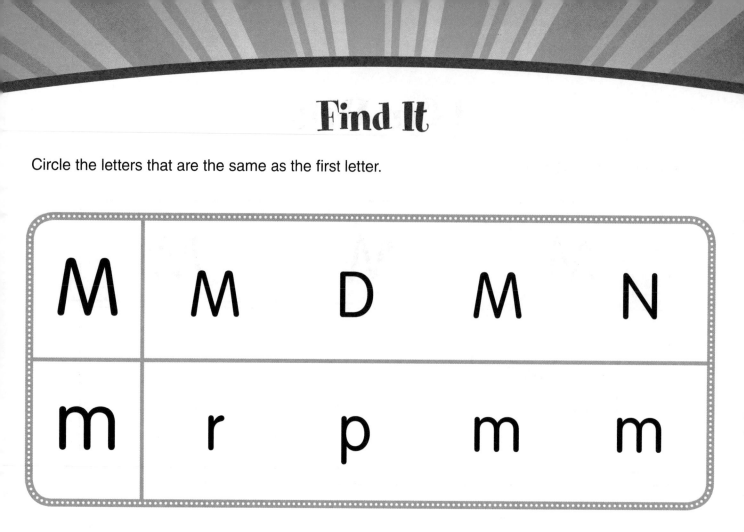

A B C D E F G H I J K L M
N O P Q R S T U V W X Y Z

a b c d e f g h i j k l m
n o p q r s t u v w x y z

Finish the Monkey

Look at the monkey.   Draw what is missing.

Trace the letters.

M M M m m m

Same Sound

Name the picture.
Color it if it begins with the same sound as *mouse*.

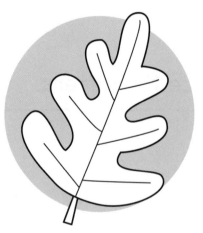

Super Skills for Summer • EMC 9830 • © Evan-Moor Corp.

Big and Little

Draw a line to make a match.

See the capital **N**.

See the lowercase **n**.

I Can Write

Trace and write the letters.

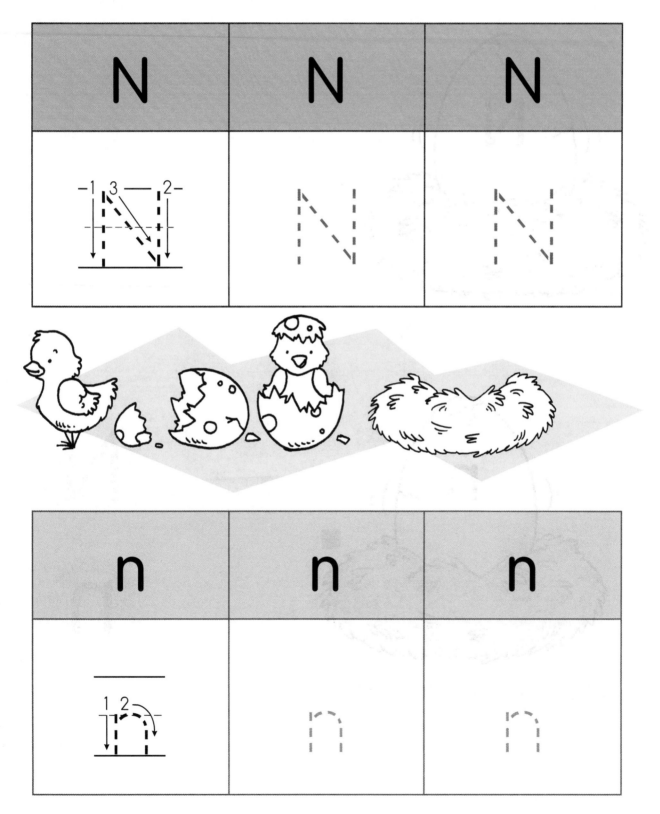

Super Skills for Summer • EMC 9830 • © Evan-Moor Corp.

Find It

Circle the letters that are the same as the first letter.

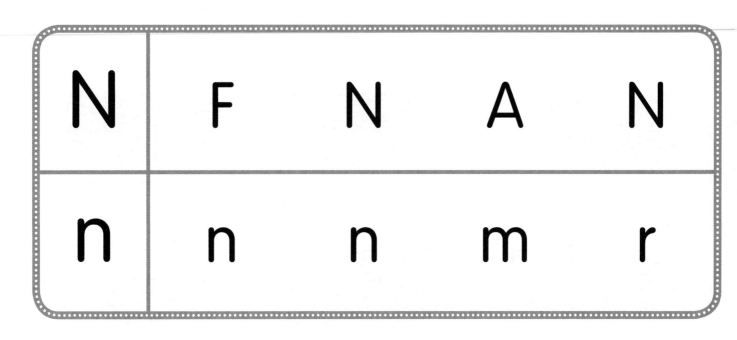

N	F	N	A	N
n	n	n	m	r

Find the big **N** and the little **n**. Circle them.

A B C D E F G H I J K L M
N O P Q R S T U V W X Y Z

a b c d e f g h i j k l m
n o p q r s t u v w x y z

Same or Different?

Circle the pictures in each row that are the same.

Trace the letters.

Same Sound

Name the picture.
Color it if it begins with the same sound as **nest** or **nightingale**.

Big and Little

Draw a line to make a match.

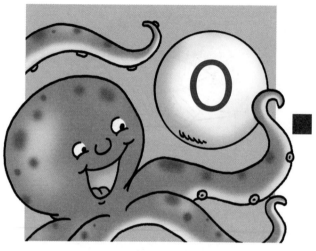

See the capital O.

See the lowercase o.

I Can Write

Trace and write the letters.

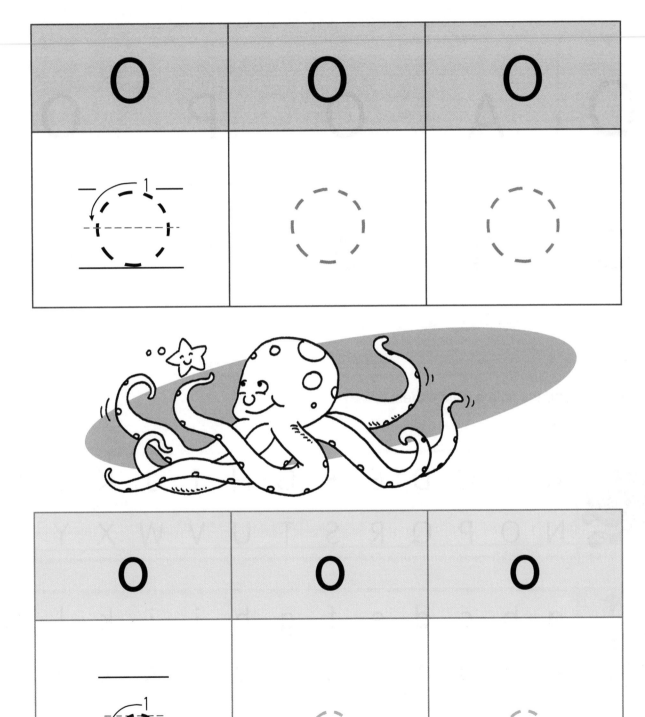

Find It

Circle the letters that are the same as the first letter.

O	A	O	P	O
o	a	o	o	c

Find the big **O** and the little **o**. Circle them.

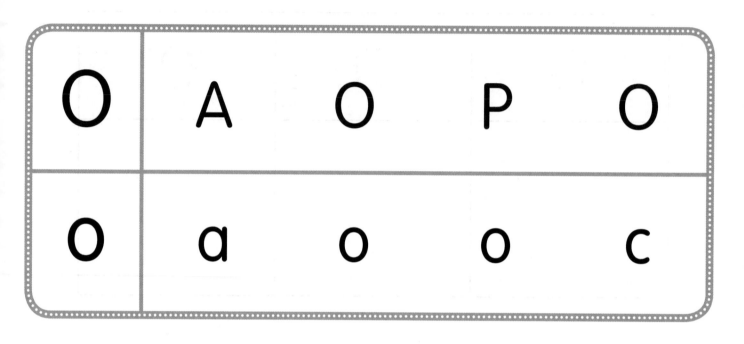

A B C D E F G H I J K L M
N O P Q R S T U V W X Y Z

a b c d e f g h i j k l m
n o p q r s t u v w x y z

Same Sound

Name the picture.
Color it if it begins with the same sound as **otter**.

Big and Little

Draw a line to make a match.

See the capital **P**.

See the lowercase **p**.

I Can Write

Trace and write the letters.

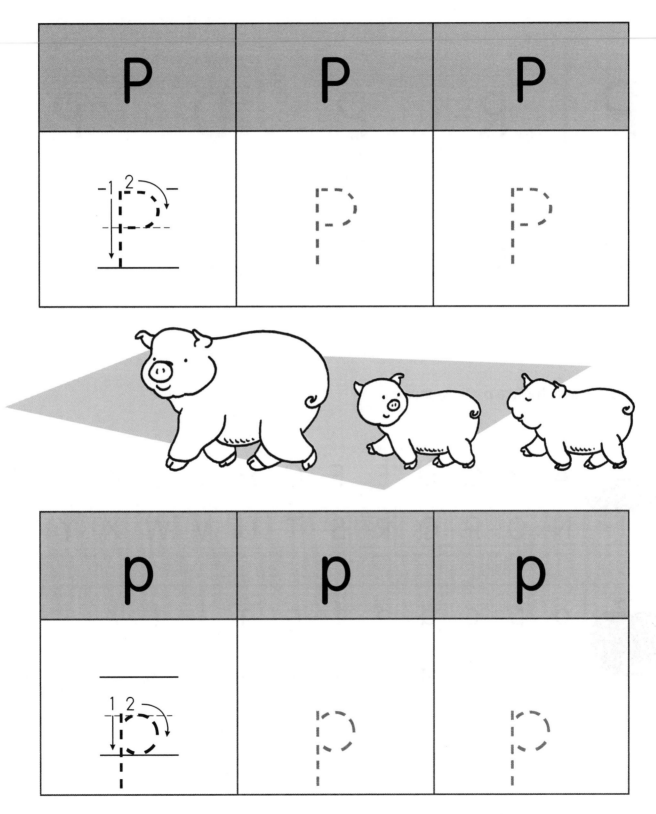

Find It

Circle the letters that are the same as the first letter.

P	R	P	D	P
p	b	p	c	p

Find the big **P** and the little **p**. Circle them.

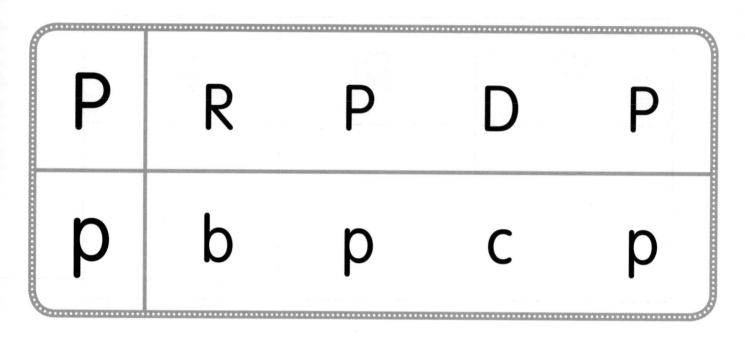

A B C D E F G H I J K L M
N O P Q R S T U V W X Y Z

a b c d e f g h i j k l m
n o p q r s t u v w x y z

Same or Different?

Circle the pictures in each row that are the same.

Trace the letters.

P P P P P P P P

Same Sound

Name the picture.
Color it if it begins with the same sound as *pig*.

Super Skills for Summer • EMC 9830 • © Evan-Moor Corp.

Big and Little

Draw a line to make a match.

See the capital **Q**.

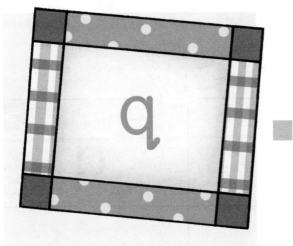

See the lowercase **q**.

I Can Write

Trace and write the letters.

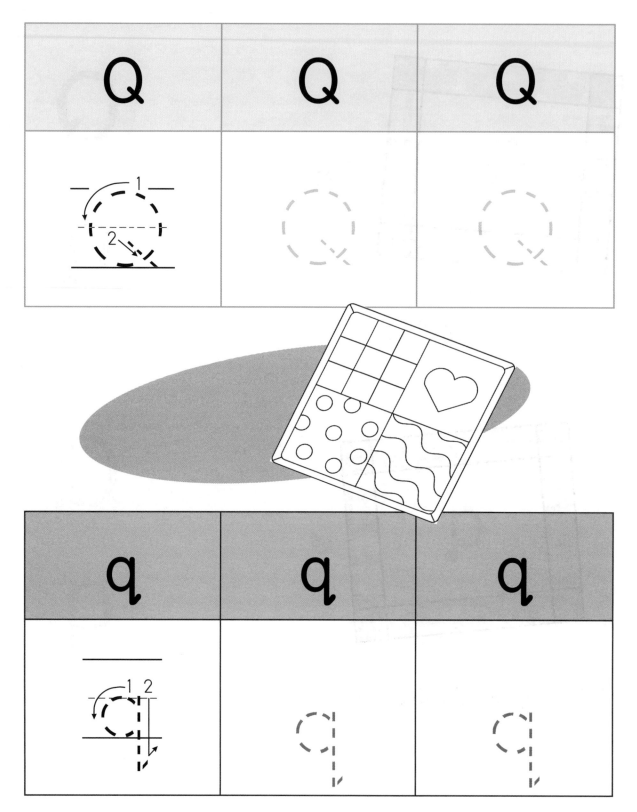

Find It

Circle the letters that are the same as the first letter.

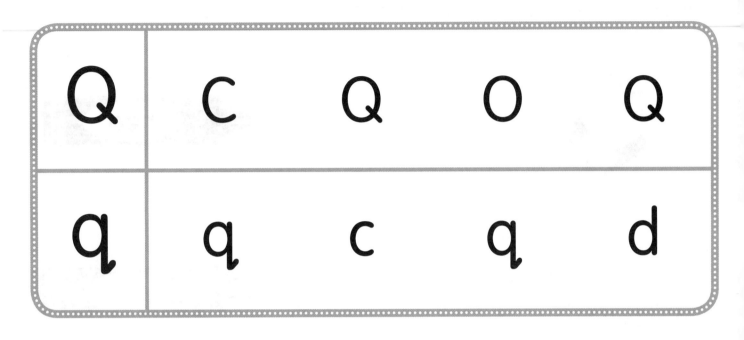

Q	C	Q	O	Q
q	q	c	q	d

Find the big **Q** and the little **q**. Circle them.

A B C D E F G H I J K L M
N O P Q R S T U V W X Y Z

a b c d e f g h i j k l m
n o p q r s t u v w x y z

Rhyme Time

Draw a line to match the pictures that rhyme.

Trace the letters.

Super Skills for Summer • EMC 9830 • © Evan-Moor Corp.

Same Sound

Name the picture.
Color it if it begins with the same sound as *quail*.

Big and Little

Draw a line to make a match.

See the capital **R**.

See the lowercase **r**.

I Can Write

Trace and write the letters.

R	R	R
	R	R

r	r	r
r	r	r

Find It

Circle the letters that are the same as the first letter.

R	F	B	R	R
r	r	c	r	n

Find the big **R** and the little **r**. Circle them.

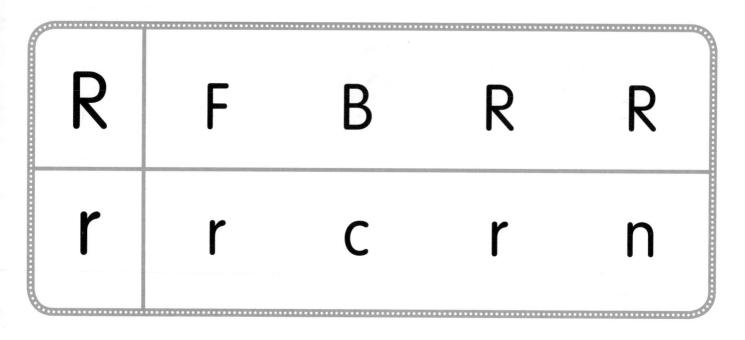

A B C D E F G H I J K L M
N O P Q R S T U V W X Y Z

a b c d e f g h i j k l m
n o p q r s t u v w x y z

Super Skills for Summer • EMC 9830 • © Evan-Moor Corp.

R Is for Rabbit

Trace the rabbit.
Color the rabbit brown.

Trace the letters.

R R R R r r r r

Same Sound

Name the picture.
Color it if it begins with the same sound as *rug*.

Super Skills for Summer • EMC 9830 • © Evan-Moor Corp.

Big and Little

Draw a line to make a match.

See the capital **S**.

See the lowercase **s**.

I Can Write

Trace and write the letters.

S	S	S
S	S	S

S	S	S
s	s	s

Super Skills for Summer • EMC 9830 • © Evan-Moor Corp.

Find It

Circle the letters that are the same as the first letter.

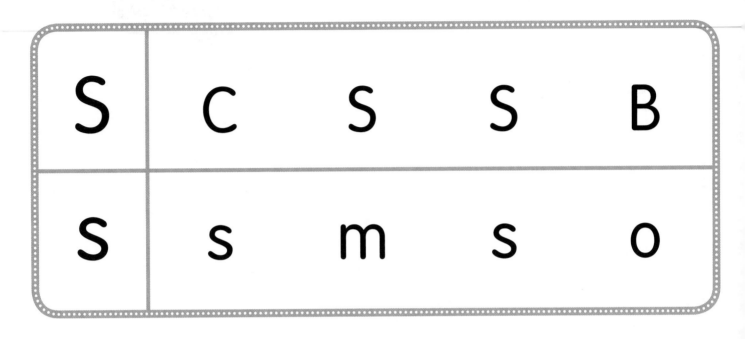

S	C	S	S	B
s	s	m	s	o

Find the big **S** and the little **s**. Circle them.

A B C D E F G H I J K L M
N O P Q R S T U V W X Y Z

a b c d e f g h i j k l m
n o p q r s t u v w x y z

It Rhymes with Sock

Color the pictures that rhyme with **sock**.

Trace the letters.

Same Sound

Name the picture.
Color it if it begins with the same sound as *sit*.

Big and Little

Draw a line to make a match.

See the capital **T**.

See the lowercase **t**.

I Can Write

Trace and write the letters.

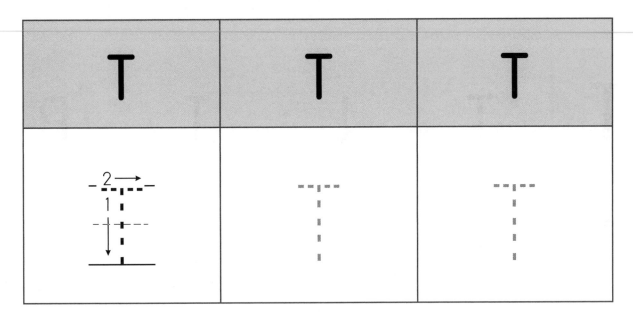

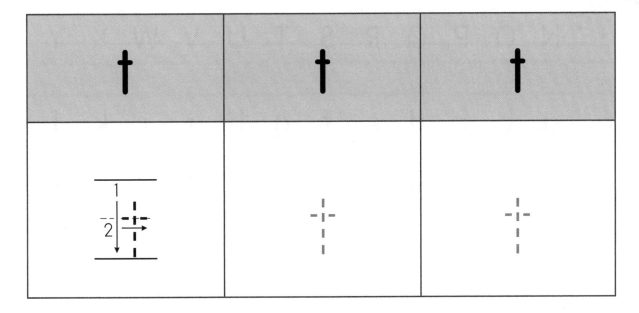

Find It

Circle the letters that are the same as the first letter.

T	T	L	T	P
t	t	x	t	i

Find the big **T** and the little **t**. Circle them.

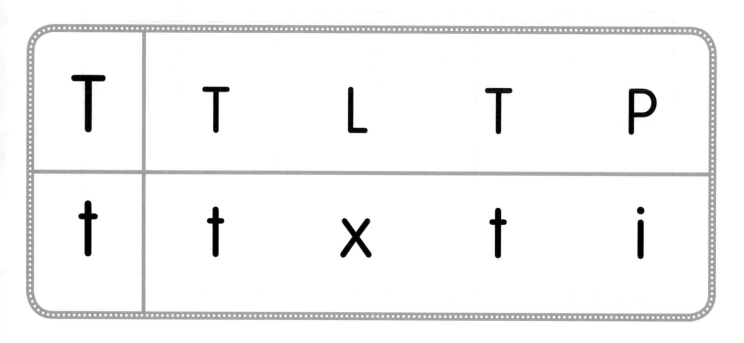

A B C D E F G H I J K L M
N O P Q R S T U V W X Y Z

a b c d e f g h i j k l m
n o p q r s t u v w x y z

Same Sound

Name the picture.
Color it if it begins with the same sound as *tug*.

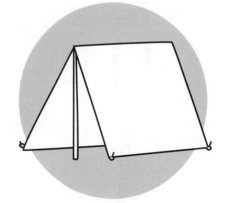

Big and Little

Draw a line to make a match.

See the capital **U**.

See the lowercase **u**.

I Can Write

Trace and write the letters.

Find It

Circle the letters that are the same as the first letter.

U	C	Q	U	U
u	q	u	u	c

Find the big **U** and the little **u**. Circle them.

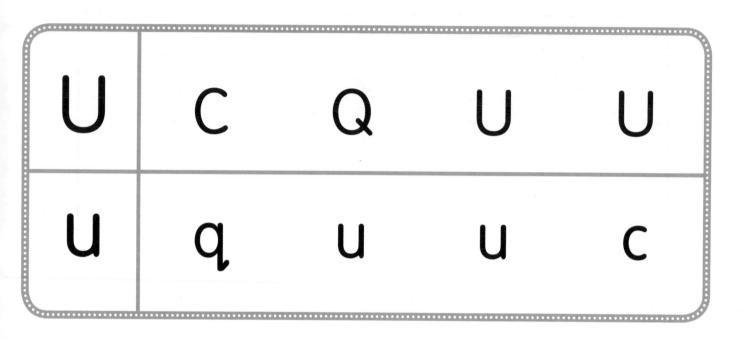

A B C D E F G H I J K L M
N O P Q R S T U V W X Y Z

a b c d e f g h i j k l m
n o p q r s t u v w x y z

Same Sound

Name the picture.
Color it if it begins with the same sound as *uncle*.

Big and Little

Draw a line to make a match.

See the capital **V**.

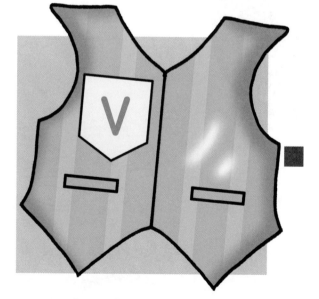

See the lowercase **v**.

I Can Write

Trace and write the letters.

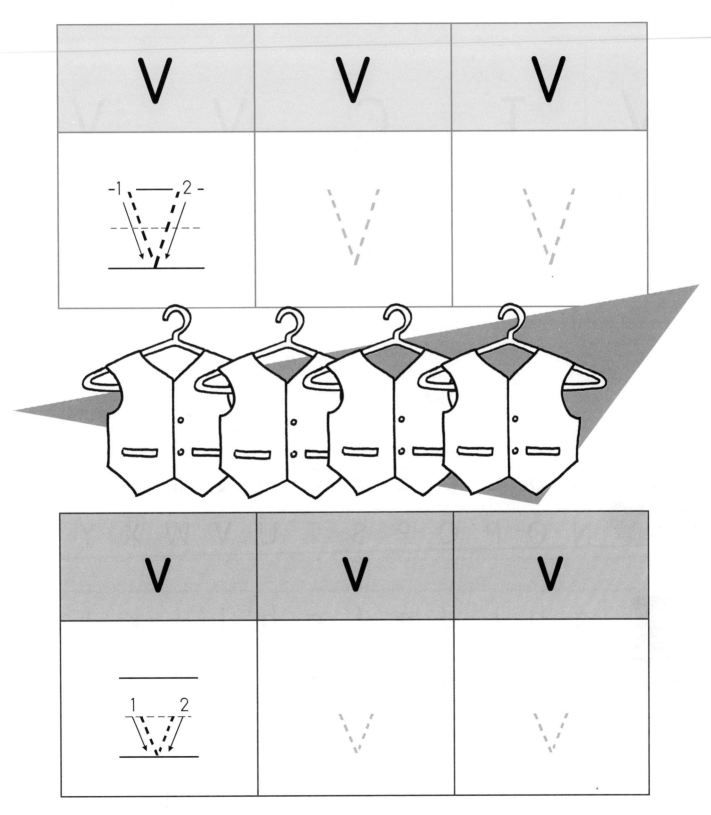

Find It

Circle the letters that are the same as the first letter.

V	T	C	V	V
v	r	v	n	v

Find the big **V** and the little **v**. Circle them.

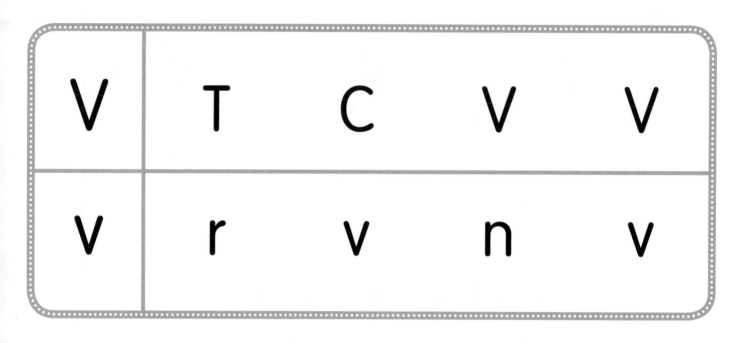

A B C D E F G H I J K L M
N O P Q R S T U V W X Y Z

a b c d e f g h i j k l m
n o p q r s t u v w x y z

V Is for Vulture

Trace the wing.
Color the vulture.

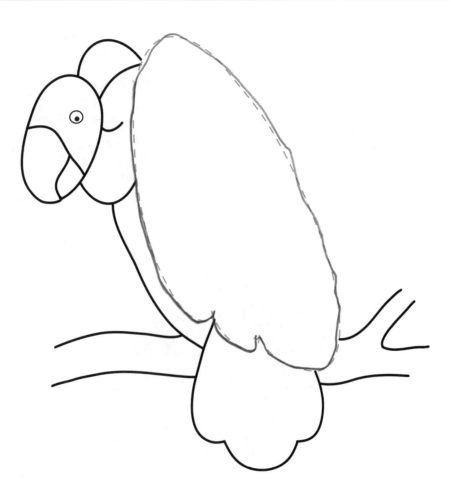

Trace the letters.

V V V v v v

Same Sound

Name the picture.
Color it if it begins with the same sound as **van**.

Big and Little

Draw a line to make a match.

See the capital **W**.

See the lowercase **w**.

I Can Write

Trace and write the letters.

Super Skills for Summer • EMC 9830 • © Evan-Moor Corp.

Find It

Circle the letters that are the same as the first letter.

W	M	W	V	W
w	w	n	m	w

Find the big **W** and the little **w**. Circle them.

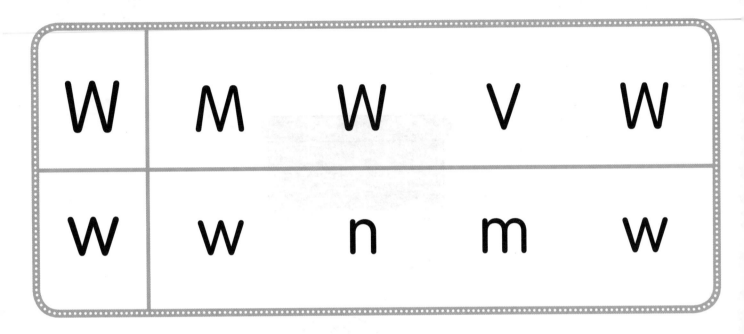

A B C D E F G H I J K L M
N O P Q R S T U V W X Y Z

a b c d e f g h i j k l m
n o p q r s t u v w x y z

Finish the Wagon

Draw what is missing.
Color it to match.

Trace the letters.

Super Skills for Summer • EMC 9830 • © Evan-Moor Corp.

Same Sound

Name the picture.
Color it if it begins with the same sound as **wag**.

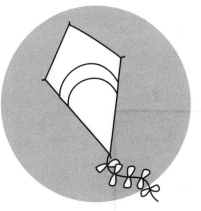

Big and Little

Draw a line to make a match.

See the capital **X**.

See the lowercase **x**.

I Can Write

Trace and write the letters.

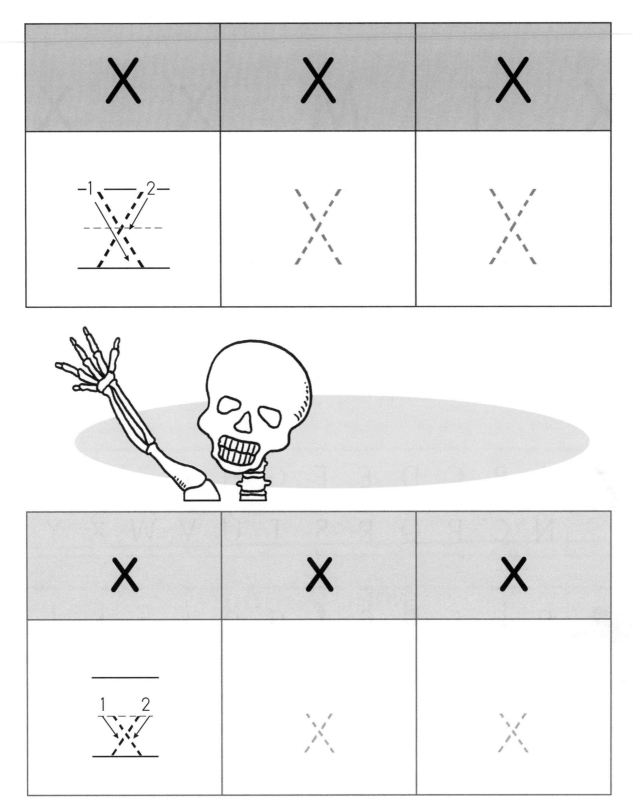

Find It

Circle the letters that are the same as the first letter.

X	T	M	X	X
x	r	x	p	x

Find the big **X** and the little **x**. Circle them.

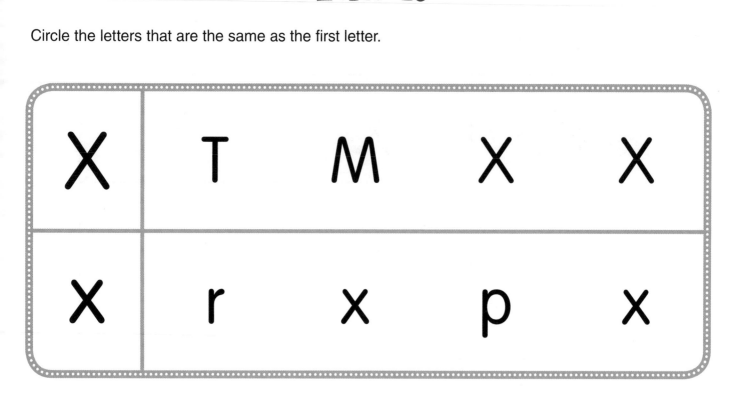

A B C D E F G H I J K L M
N O P Q R S T U V W X Y Z

a b c d e f g h i j k l m
n o p q r s t u v w x y z

Finish the Fox

Draw what is missing.
Color to match.

Trace the letters.

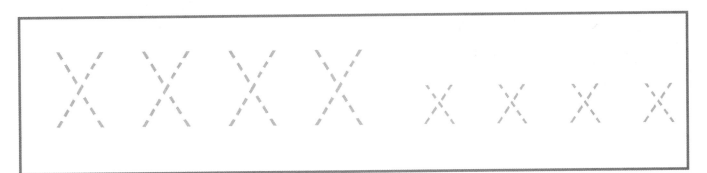

Same Sound

Name the picture.
Color it if it ends with the same sound as *fox*.

Super Skills for Summer • EMC 9830 • © Evan-Moor Corp.

Big and Little

Draw a line to make a match.

See the capital **Y**.

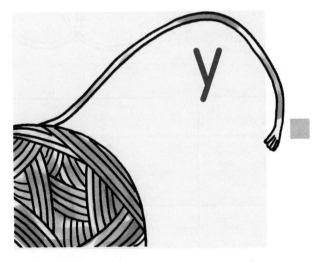

See the lowercase **y**.

I Can Write

Trace and write the letters.

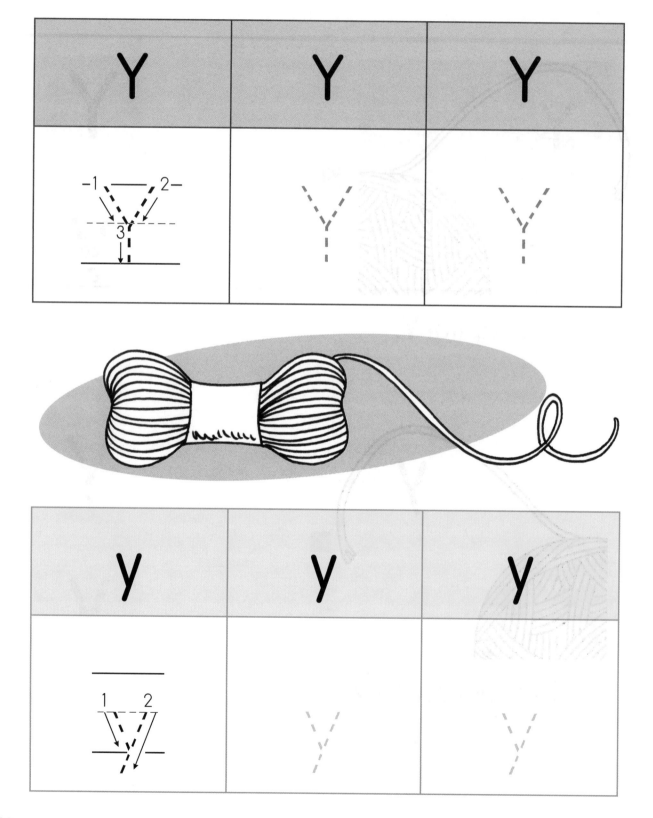

Super Skills for Summer • EMC 9830 • © Evan-Moor Corp.

Find It

Circle the letters that are the same as the first letter.

Y	Y	M	P	Y
y	x	y	y	w

Find the big **Y** and the little **y**. Circle them.

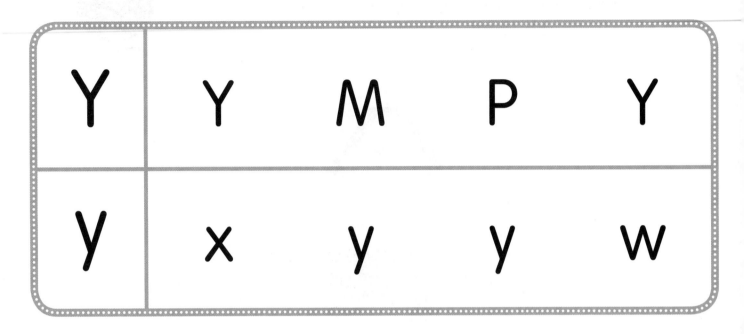

A B C D E F G H I J K L M
N O P Q R S T U V W X Y Z

a b c d e f g h i j k l m
n o p q r s t u v w x y z

Find the Rhyme

Connect the dots to complete the picture that rhymes with **yarn**.

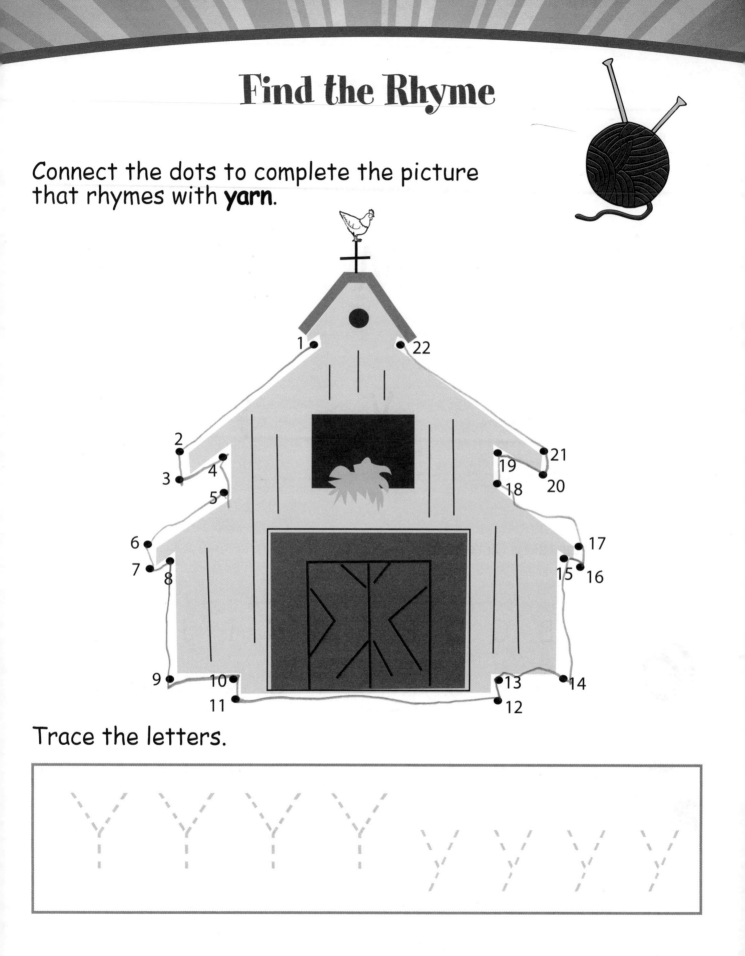

Trace the letters.

Y Y Y Y Y Y Y Y

Same Sound

Name the picture.
Color it if it begins with the same sound as *yellow*.

Big and Little

Draw a line to make a match.

See the capital **Z**.

See the lowercase **z**.

Super Skills for Summer • EMC 9830 • © Evan-Moor Corp.

I Can Write

Trace and write the letters.

Z	Z	Z
Z	Z	Z

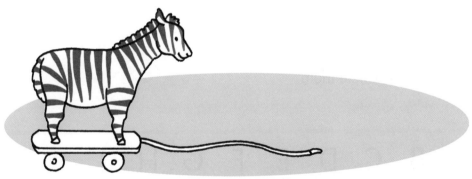

Z	Z	Z
Z	Z	Z

Find It

Circle the letters that are the same as the first letter.

Z	Z	N	Z	L
z	z	r	y	z

Find the big **Z** and the little **z**. Circle them.

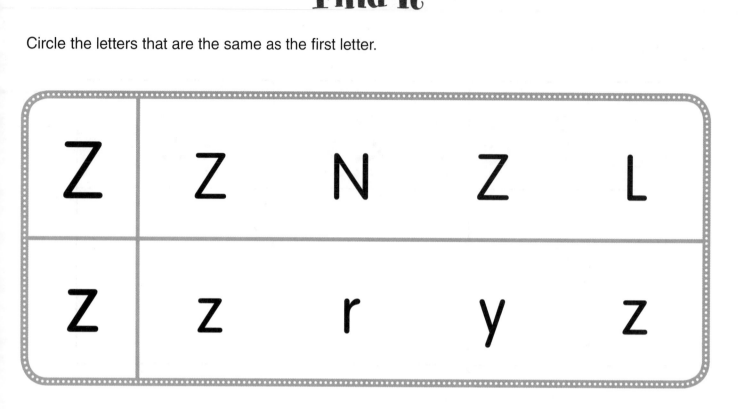

A B C D E F G H I J K L M
N O P Q R S T U V W X Y Z

a b c d e f g h i j k l m
n o p q r s t u v w x y z

Black and White

A zebra is black and white.
Draw another black and white animal.

Trace the letters.

Same Sound

Name the picture.
Color it if it begins with the same sound as *zoo*.

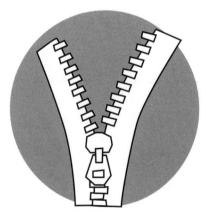

Super Skills for Summer • EMC 9830 • © Evan-Moor Corp.

Learning Center

Use a pocket folder and an envelope to assemble a fun, self-contained learning center that your child can play with over and over again.

Alphabet Card Games

What's My Name?
Use the alphabet cards to introduce the names of the letters, both uppercase and lowercase.

Make a Match
Children match a lowercase and uppercase letter. They then turn the cards over to self-check. If a correct match has been made, the child will see a picture of the same object whose name begins with the letter being matched.

First-Sound Game
Use the alphabet cards as phonics flashcards and ask children to identify the sound of each letter.

ABC Order
Children take all of the uppercase or lowercase cards and place them in alphabetical order.

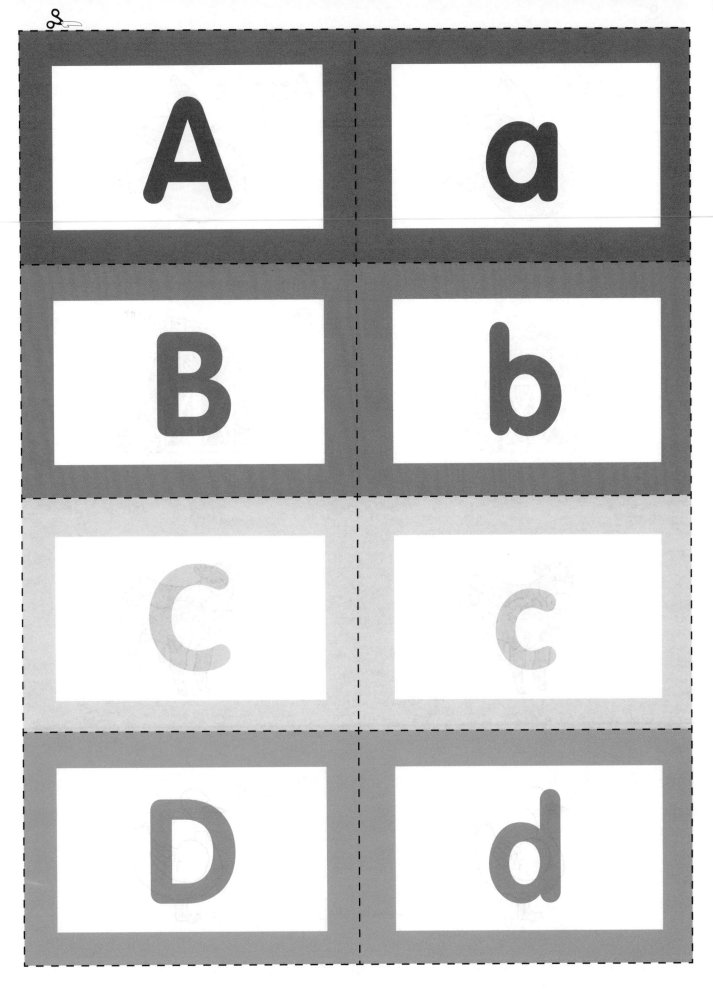

apple

Apple

barn

Barn

cow

Cow

duck

Duck

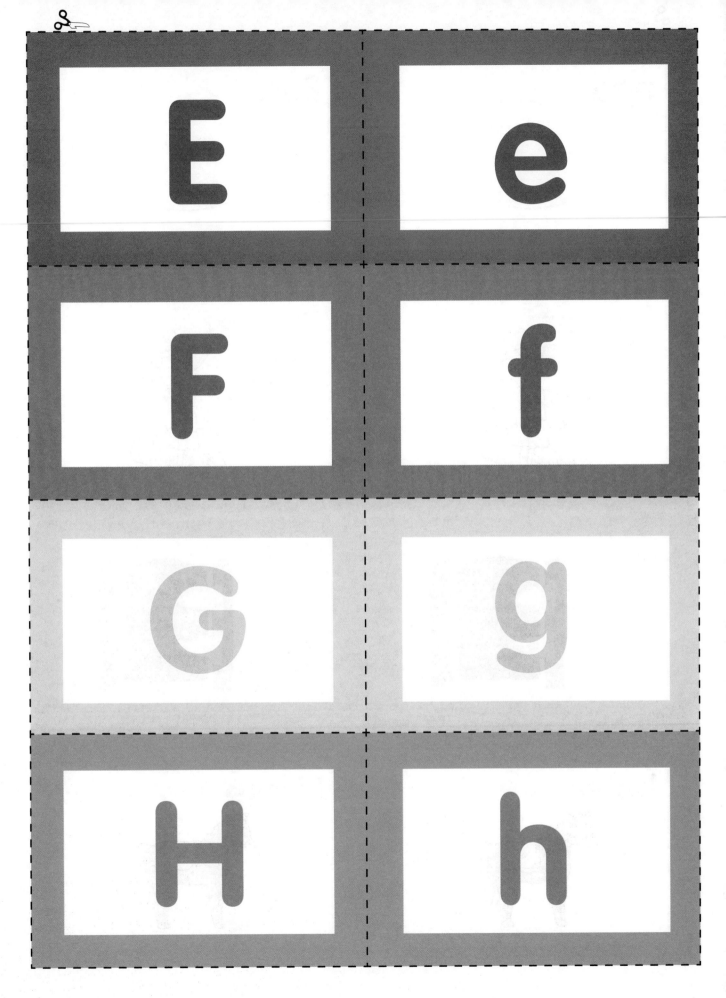

egg

Egg

farmer

Farmer

gate

Gate

horse

Horse

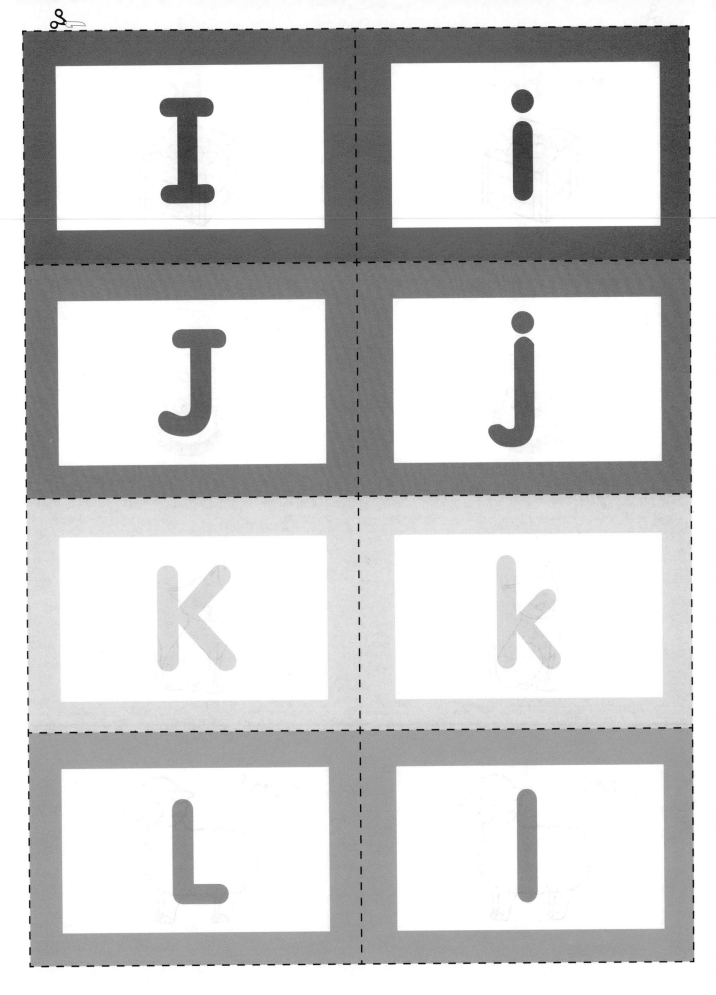

in the box

In the box

jam

Jam

kitten

Kitten

lamb

Lamb

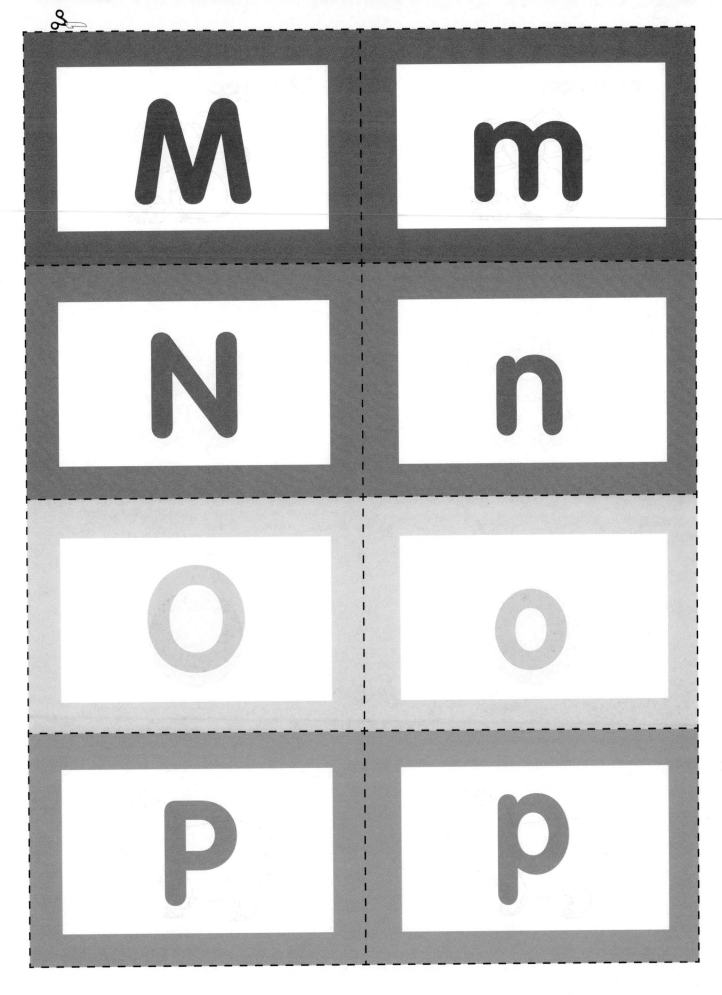

mouse

Mouse

nest

Nest

orange

Orange

pig

Pig

138

Q q

R r

S s

T t

quilt

Quilt

rooster

Rooster

seeds

Seeds

table

Table

Super Skills for Summer • EMC 9830 • © Evan-Moor Corp.

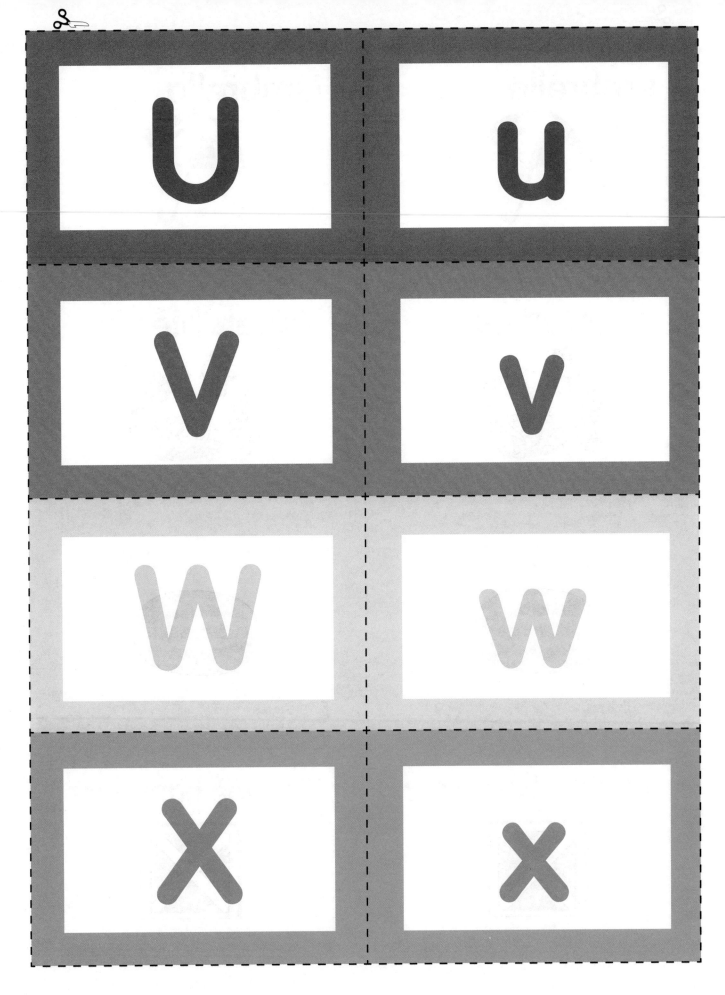

umbrella

Umbrella

vegetables

Vegetables

watermelon

Watermelon

x on the barn door

X on the barn door

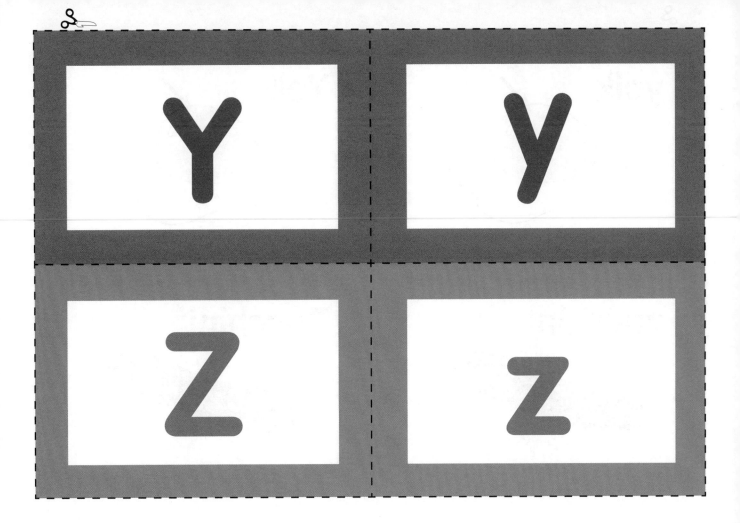

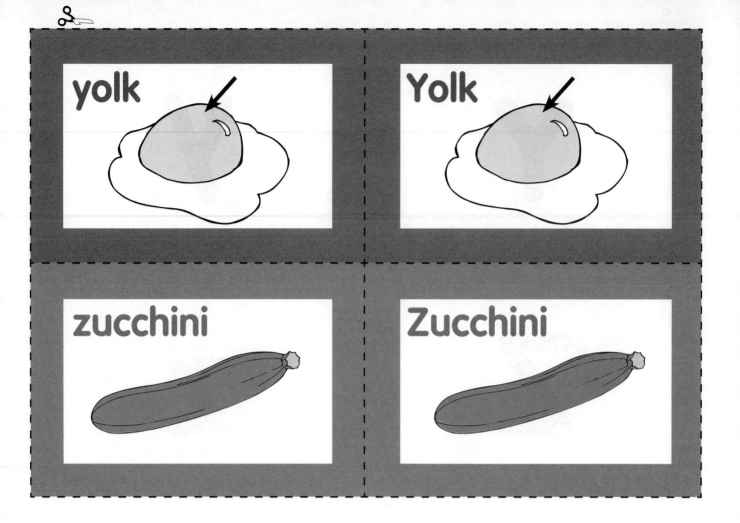

yolk

Yolk

zucchini

Zucchini

SECTION

2

Colors

Colors

Color the balloon **red**.

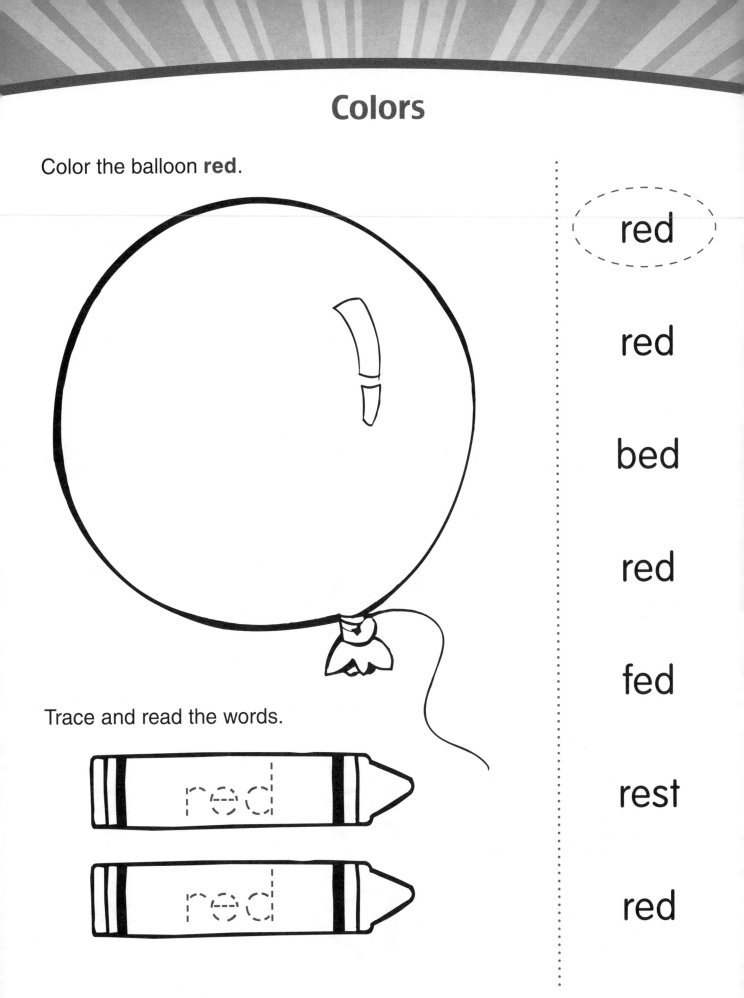

Trace and read the words.

red

red

bed

red

fed

rest

red

Colors

Color the ● s **green**.

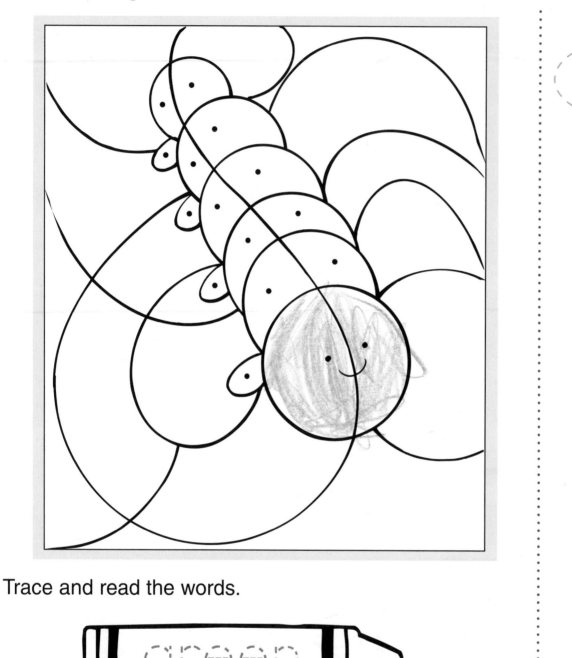

green

green

red

green

seen

red

green

Trace and read the words.

Colors

Color the ● s yellow.

yellow

yellow

green

yell

yellow

red

yellow

Trace and read the words.

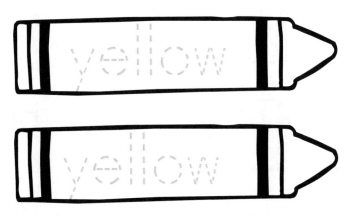

Colors

Color the bird **blue**.

blue

blue

red

yellow

blue

green

blue

Trace and read the words.

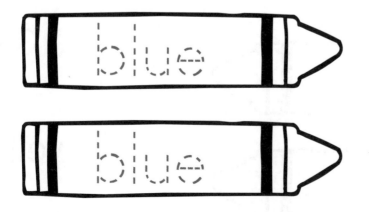

Colors

Color the butterfly **orange**.

orange

orange

green

yellow

orange

green

orange

Trace and read the words.

Colors

Color the ● s **black**. Color the ■ s **blue**.

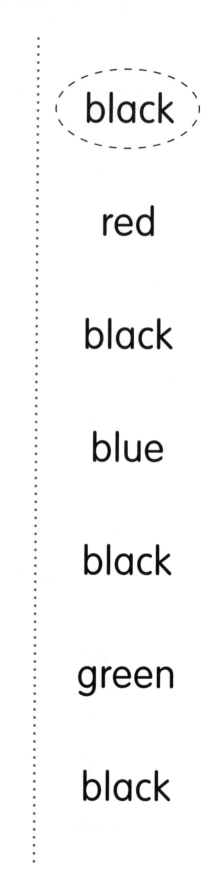

black

red

black

blue

black

green

black

Trace and read the words.

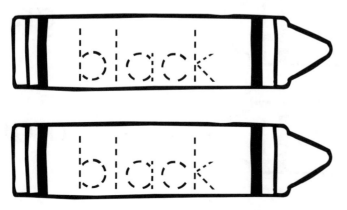

Super Skills for Summer • EMC 9830 • © Evan-Moor Corp.

Colors

Color the ● s **brown**. Color the ■ s **red**.

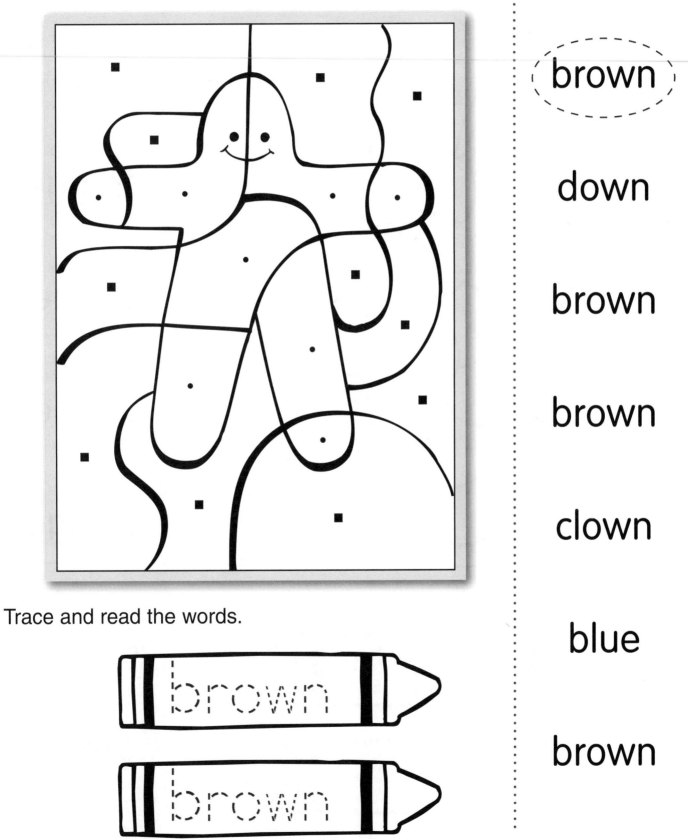

brown

down

brown

brown

clown

blue

brown

Trace and read the words.

Colors

Color the grapes **purple**.

purple

orange

purple

purple

orange

purple

green

Trace and read the words.

Colors

Color the ● s **blue**. The clouds are white .

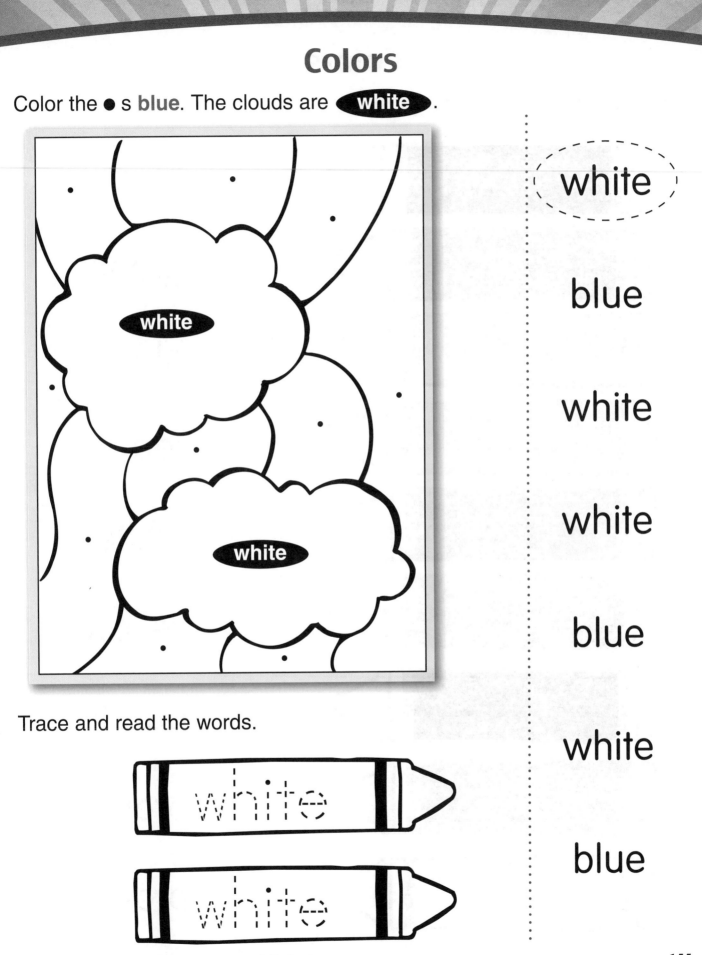

white

blue

white

white

blue

white

blue

Trace and read the words.

Colors

Draw lines to match each color.

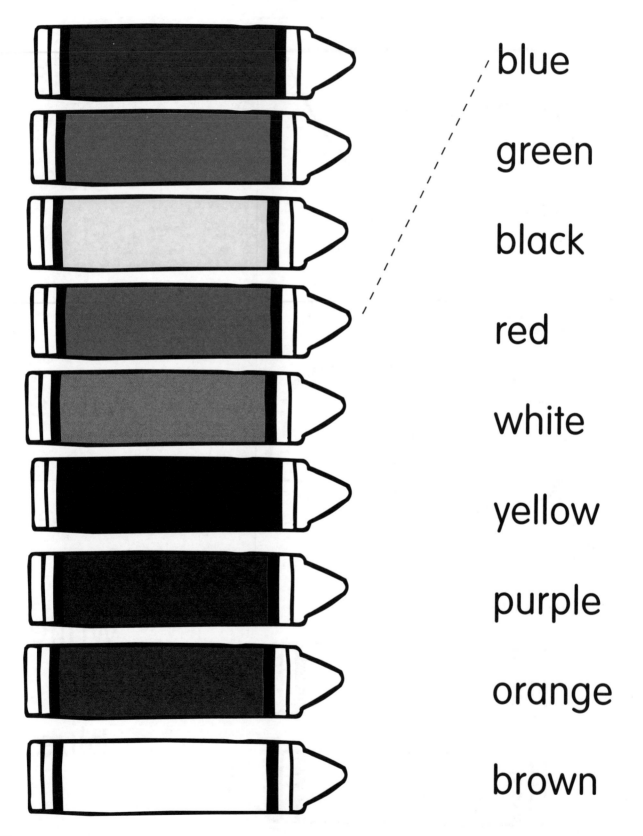

blue

green

black

red

white

yellow

purple

orange

brown

Super Skills for Summer • EMC 9830 • © Evan-Moor Corp.

Colors

Color the picture.

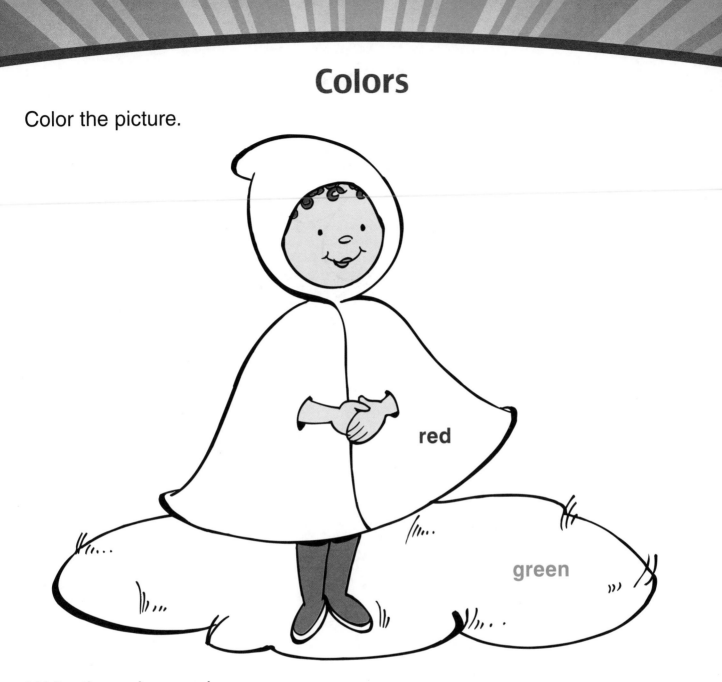

red

green

Write the color words.

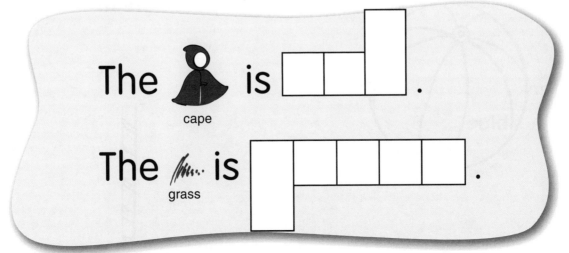

The 🧥 is [ ][ ][ ].
cape

The 🌱 is [ ][ ][ ][ ][ ].
grass

Colors

Trace the circles. Color them all.

Super Skills for Summer • EMC 9830 • © Evan-Moor Corp.

Colors

Color the picture.

yellow

green

Write the color words.

The 🐥 (chick) is y e l l o u .

The 🌱 (grass) is g r e e n .

Colors

Color the shapes.

Super Skills for Summer • EMC 9830 • © Evan-Moor Corp.

Colors

Color the picture.

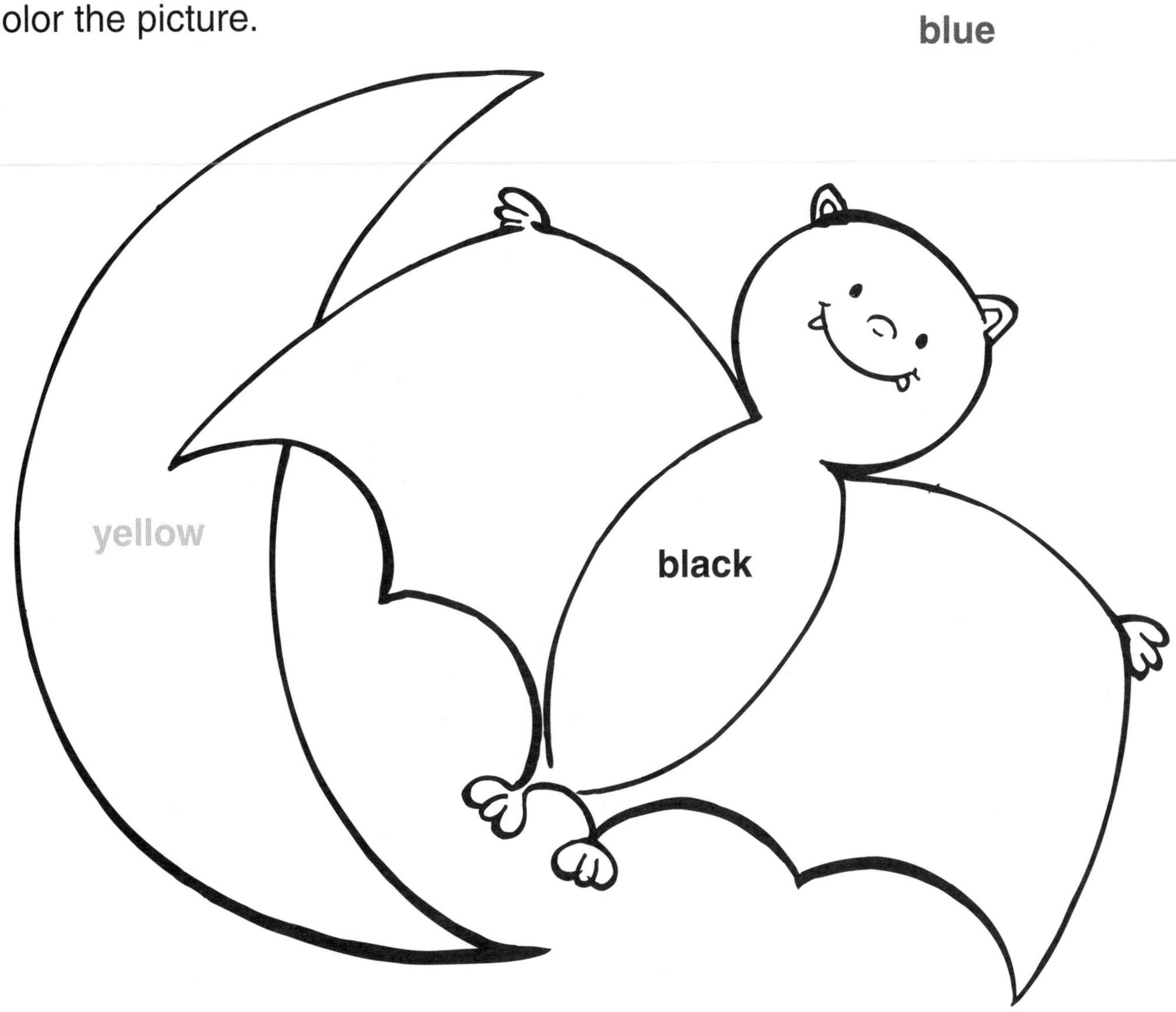

blue

yellow

black

Write the color words.

The 🦇 is ☐☐☐☐☐ .
bat

The 🌙 is ☐☐☐☐ .
moon

Colors

Trace the shapes. Color the elephant.

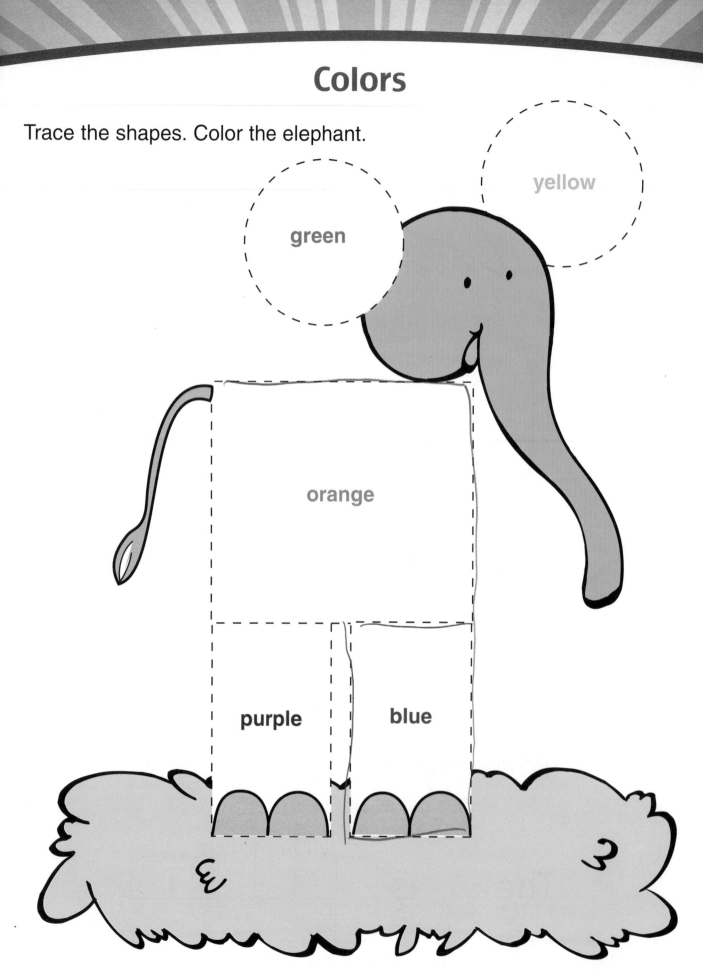

green

yellow

orange

purple

blue

Colors

Color the picture.

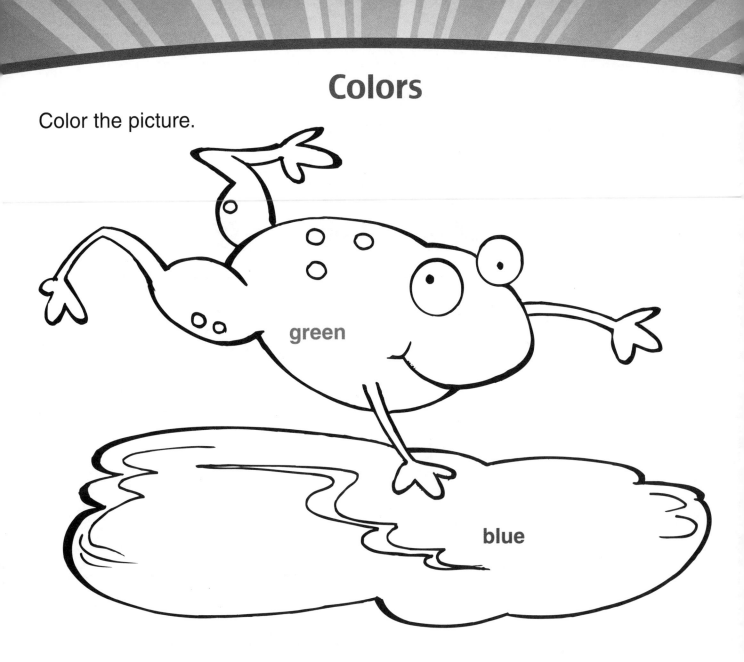

green

blue

Write the color words.

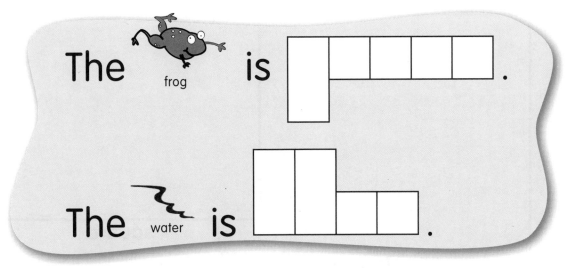

The 🐸 is ▢▢▢▢▢ .

frog

The 〰 is ▢▢▢ .

water

Colors

Name the shapes. Color the shapes to match.

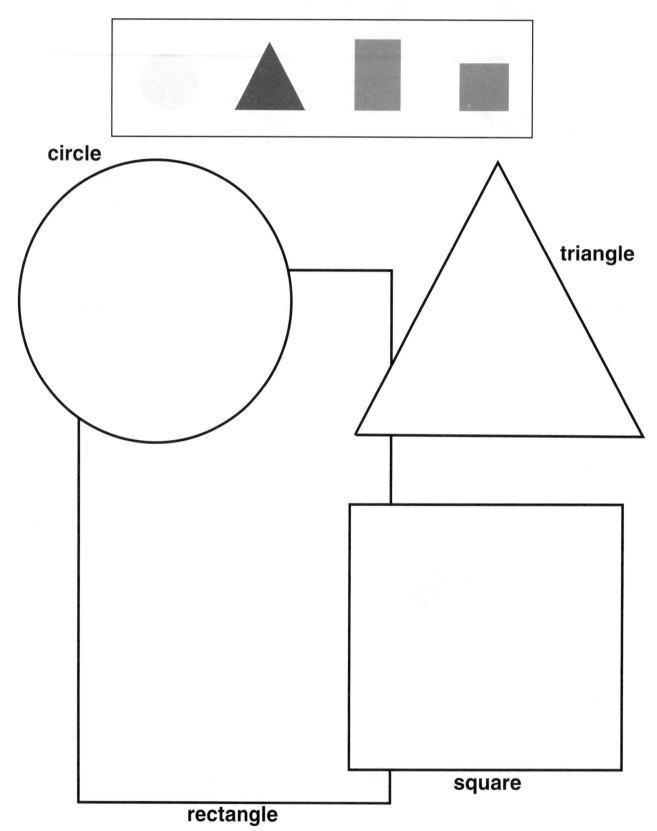

circle

triangle

square

rectangle

Colors

Color the picture.

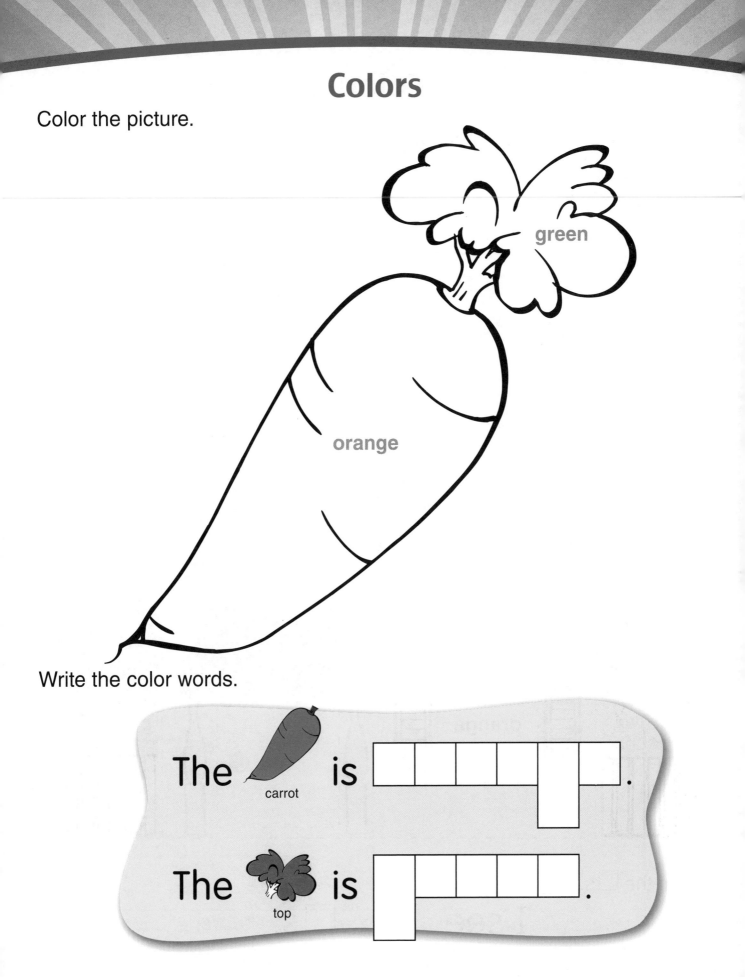

green

orange

Write the color words.

The 🥕 is ⬜⬜⬜⬜⬜⬜ .
carrot

The 🥬 is ⬜⬜⬜⬜⬜ .
top

Colors

Trace the squares. Color them all.

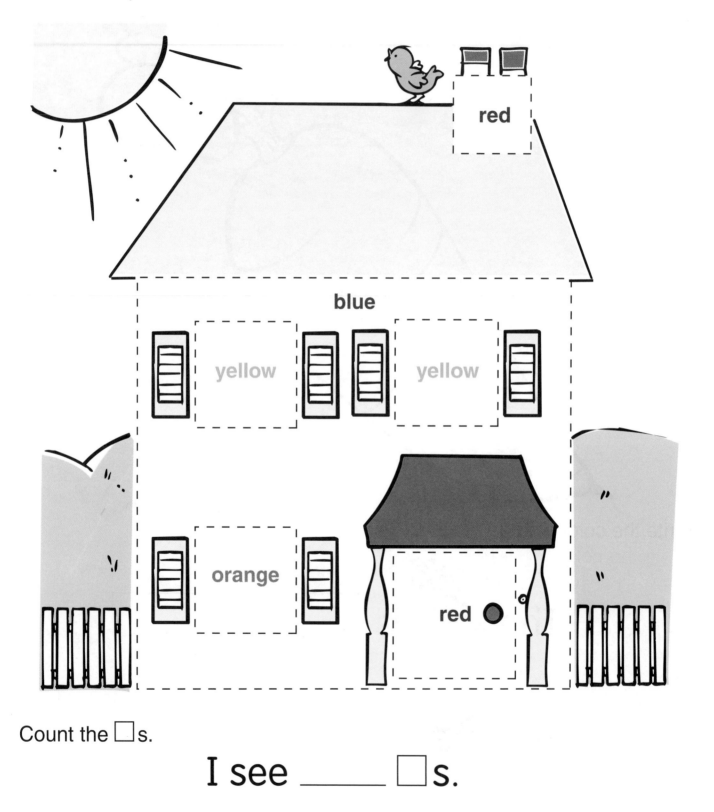

red

blue

yellow   yellow

orange   red

Count the ☐s.

I see _____ ☐s.

Colors

Color the picture. Make a **blue** coat on the bear.

brown

green

Write the color words.

The coat is _____.

The bear is _____.

Colors

Color the shapes.

Super Skills for Summer • EMC 9830 • © Evan-Moor Corp.

Math

1 Monkey

Color the monkey.

Trace.

2 Bananas

Color the bananas.

Trace.

How Many?

Count. Circle the number.

Monkey Parade

Count. Write the number.

Count and circle.

1   2   1   2   1   2

Super Skills for Summer • EMC 9830 • © Evan-Moor Corp.

Yummy Cookies

Color the cookies.

Trace.

3 3 3 3 3

How Many Cookies?

Count the cookies. Circle the number.

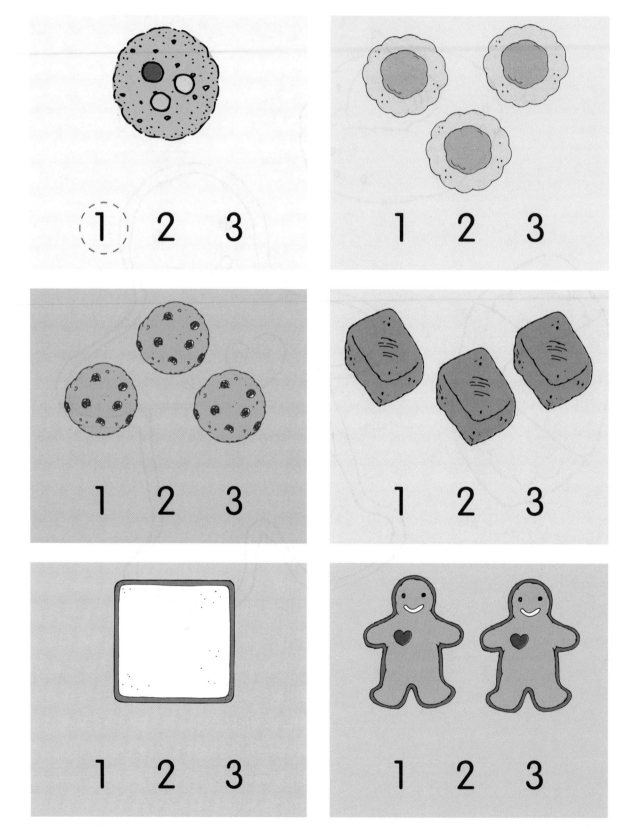

Super Skills for Summer • EMC 9830 • © Evan-Moor Corp.

In the Cookie Jar

Draw the cookies.

2

3

I Want a Cookie!

Connect the dots.

Cookies for Sale

Draw a line to make a match.

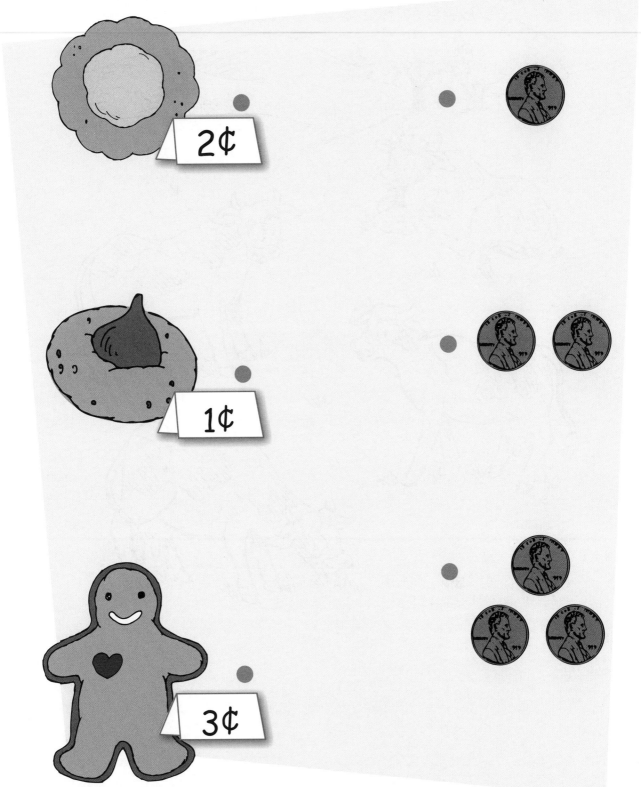

Count the Cows

Color the cows.

Trace.

L-+ L-+ L-+ L-+ L-+ L-+

Flock of Chickens

Count the chickens. Circle the number.

Feed the Pigs

Make a match.

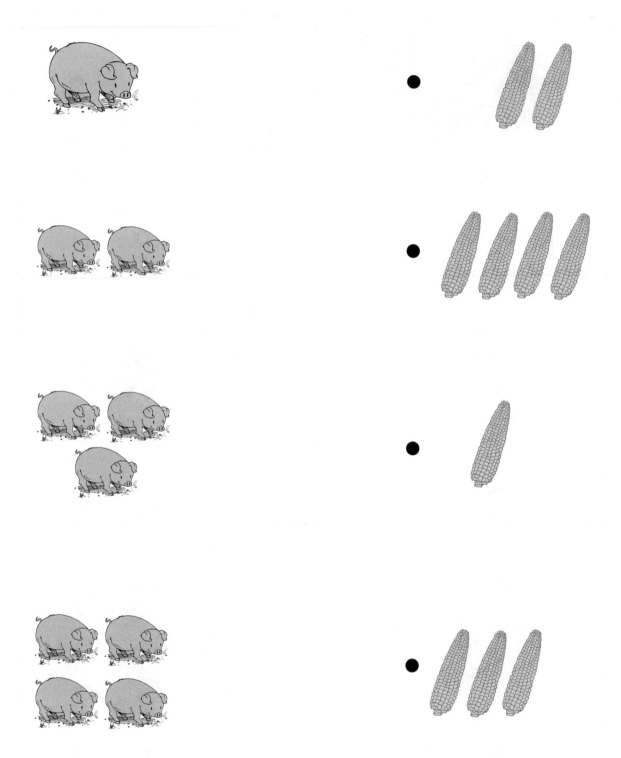

Super Skills for Summer • EMC 9830 • © Evan-Moor Corp.

Ducks at the Pond

Trace the numbers.

Write the numbers.

Pigs in Pens

Cut and glue 1 more pig into each pen.

How many pigs?

1 2 3 4

How many pigs?

1 2 3 4

Super Skills for Summer • EMC 9830 • © Evan-Moor Corp.

Red Barn

Connect the dots.
Color the barn.

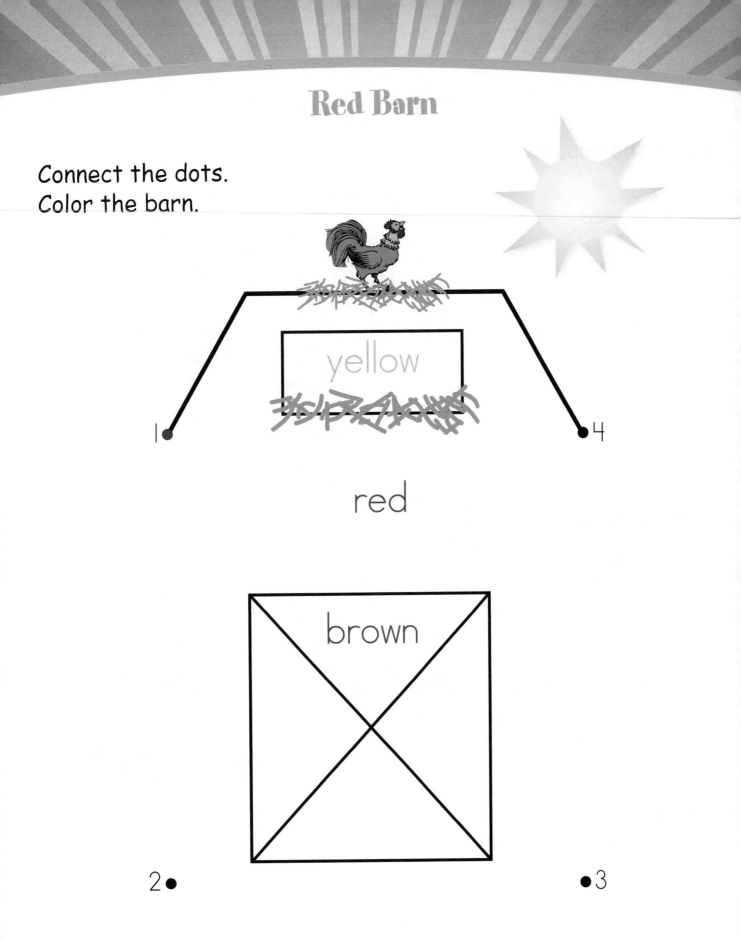

yellow

red

brown

Pet Puppies

Color the puppies.

Trace.

5 5 5 5 5 5

Super Skills for Summer • EMC 9830 • © Evan-Moor Corp.

Feed the Puppy

Look at the number on each bowl.
Cut and glue the correct number of
bones in each bowl.

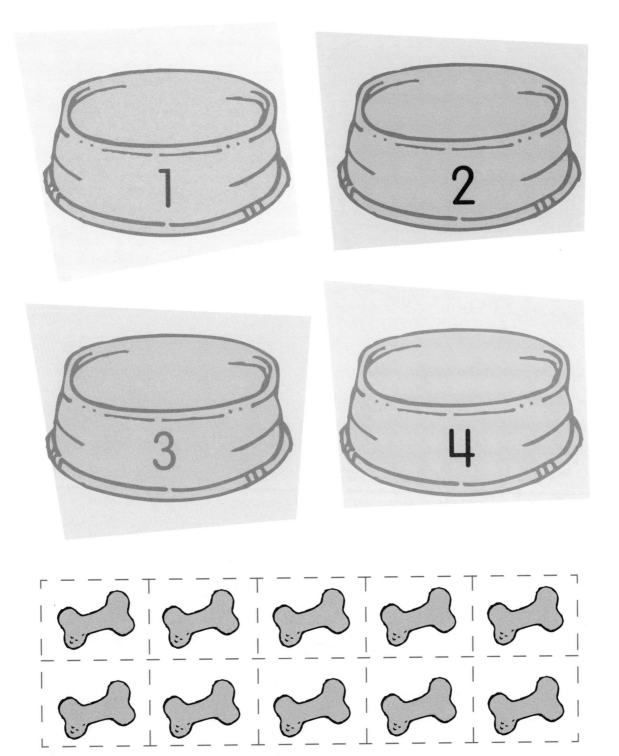

How Many Puppies?

Count the puppies. Circle the number.

1 2 3 4 5

1 2 3 4 5

1 2 3 4 5

1 2 3 4 5

1 2 3 4 5

1 2 3 4 5

Go Home, Puppy

Connect the dots.

Super Skills for Summer • EMC 9830 • © Evan-Moor Corp.

Count to 5

Trace the numbers.
Write the number on each doghouse.

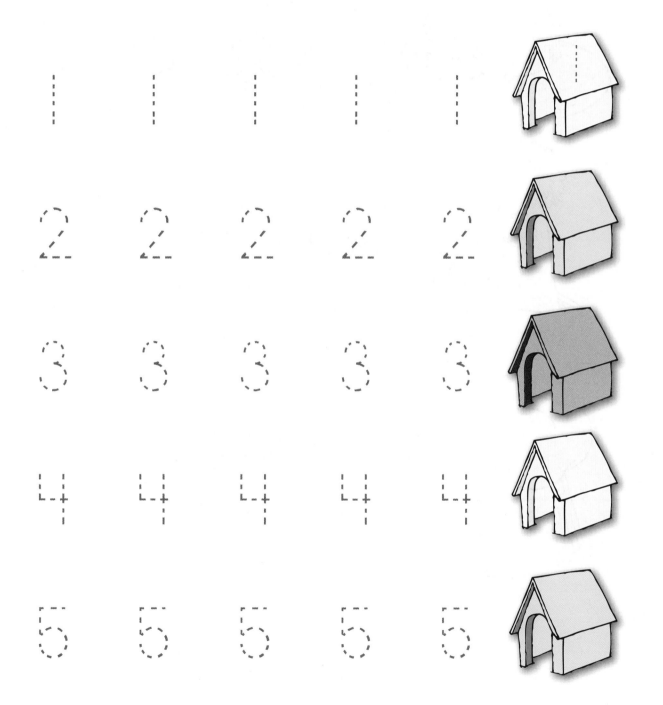

1 1 1 1 1

2 2 2 2 2

3 3 3 3 3

4 4 4 4 4

5 5 5 5 5

Hats for Sale

Color the hats.

Trace.

Super Skills for Summer • EMC 9830 • © Evan-Moor Corp.

Fancy Hats

Look at the number in each box.
Draw the correct number of flowers on each hat.

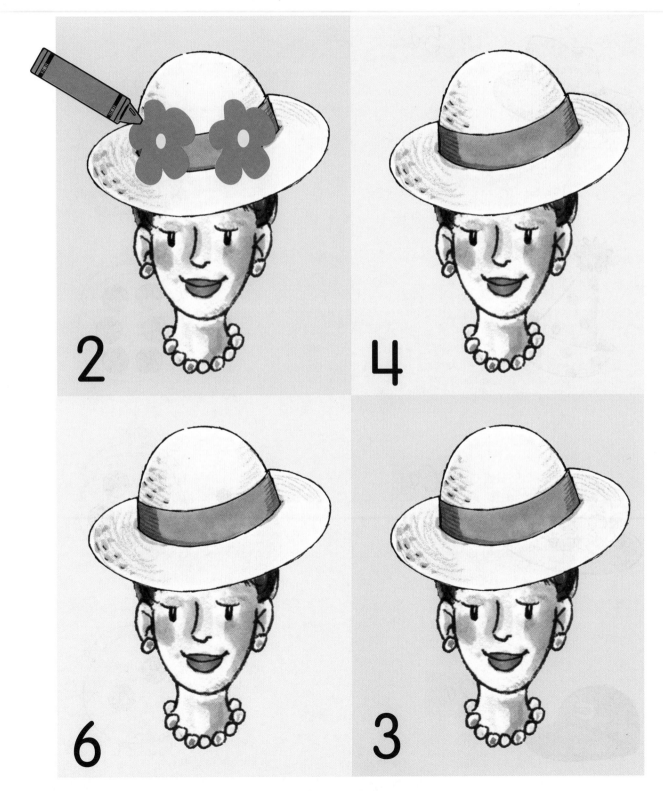

Hats for Sale

Make a match.

5¢

3¢

6¢

2¢

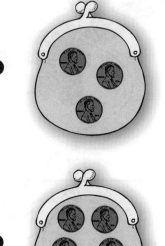

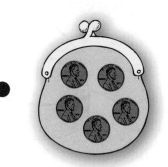

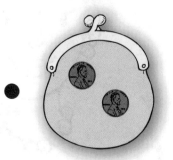

Tall Hats

How many pennies tall is the hat?

Ladybugs

Color the ladybugs.

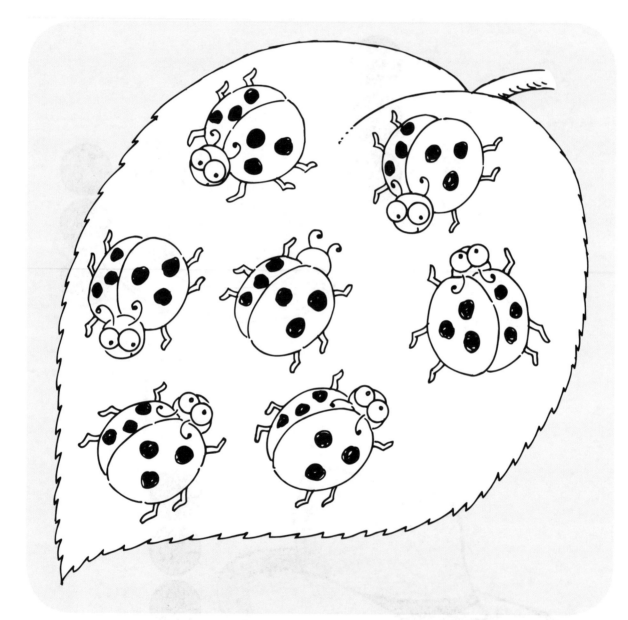

Trace.

7 7 7 7 7

Ladybug Babies

Draw a line from each ladybug to her baby or babies.

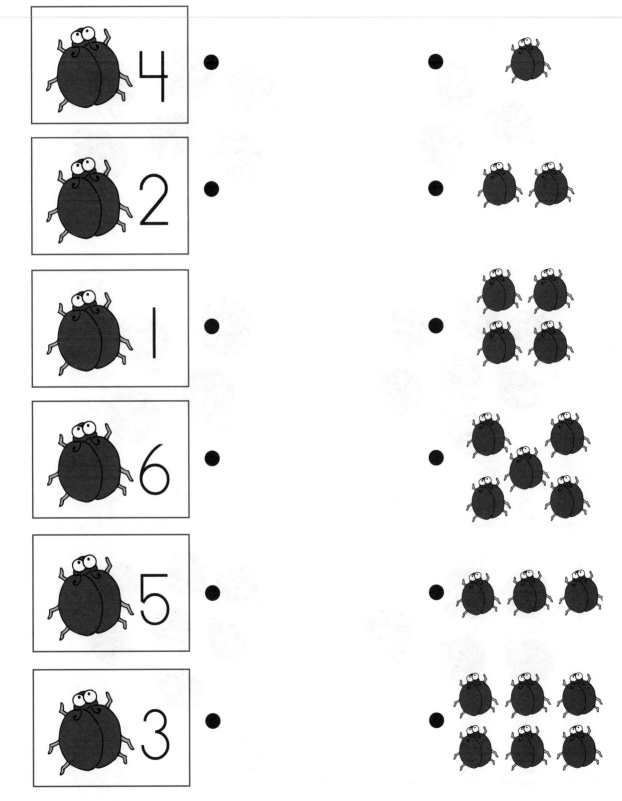

How Many?

Count the ladybugs in each box.
Circle the correct number in each box.

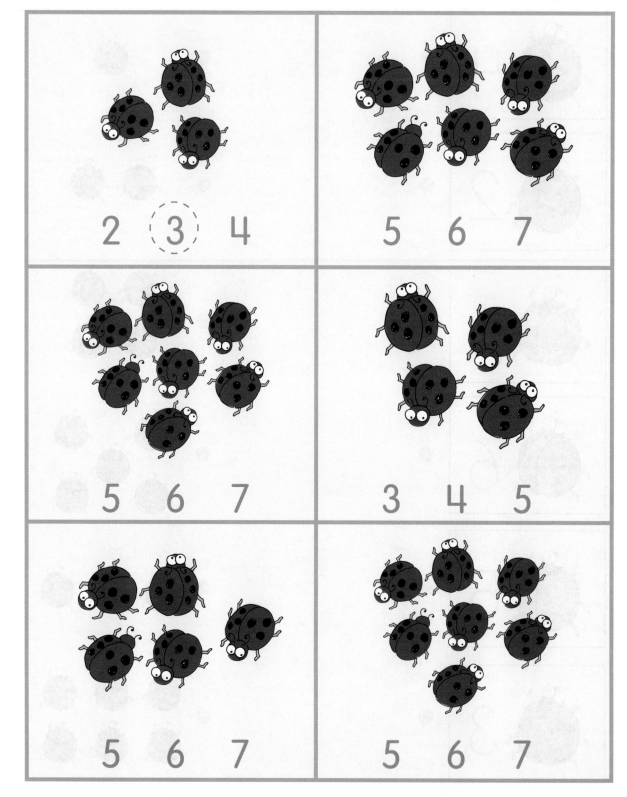

2   (3)   4

5   6   7

5   6   7

3   4   5

5   6   7

5   6   7

In the Jar

Look at the number below each jar.
Cut out the correct number of ladybugs
and glue them in each jar.

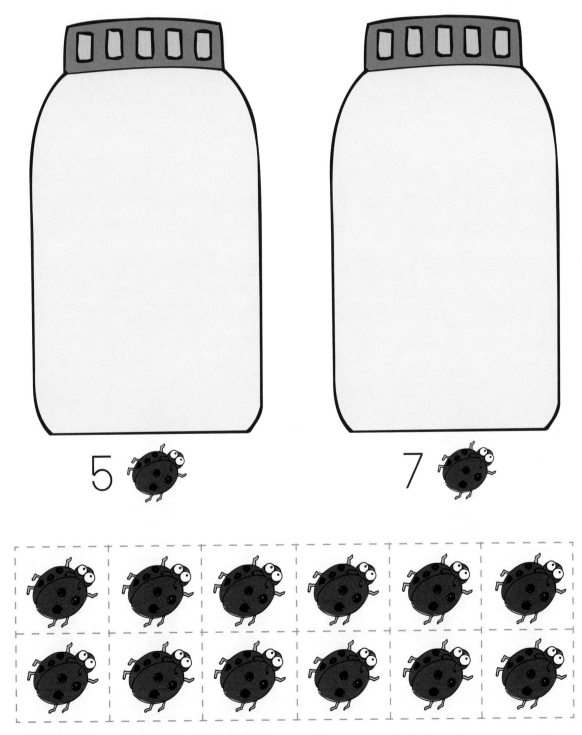

5

7

Super Skills for Summer • EMC 9830 • © Evan-Moor Corp.

Where Are the Ladybugs?

Connect the dots. Color the picture.

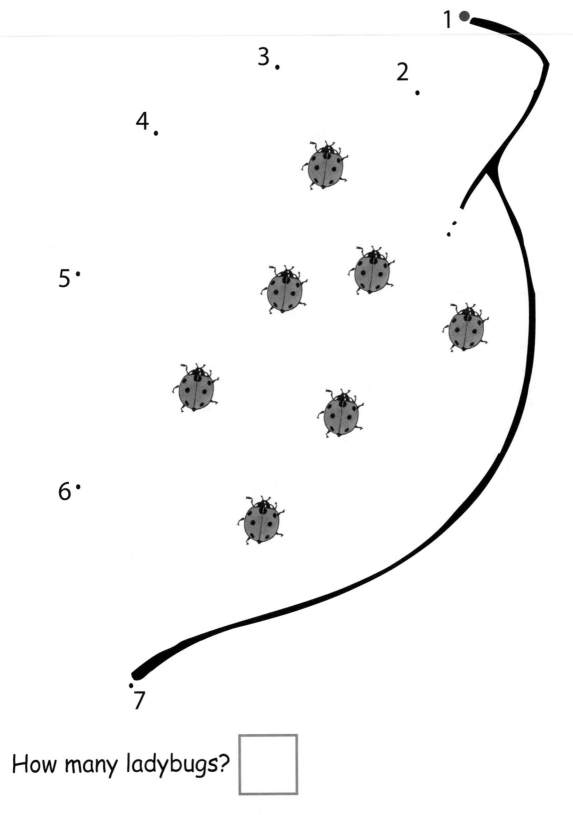

How many ladybugs?

In the Pond

Color the frogs.

Trace.

Hop to the Lily Pad

Draw a line. Match.

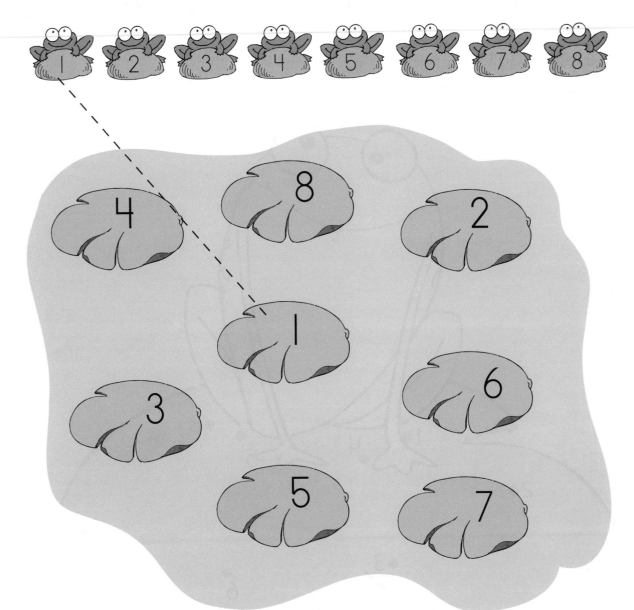

Finish the Frog

1 2 3 4 5 6 7 8

Connect the dots.
Color the frog green.

How Many?

Count the frogs. Write the number.

How many?

Which Is More?

Count the flies.
Write the number in the box.
Color the set that is more.

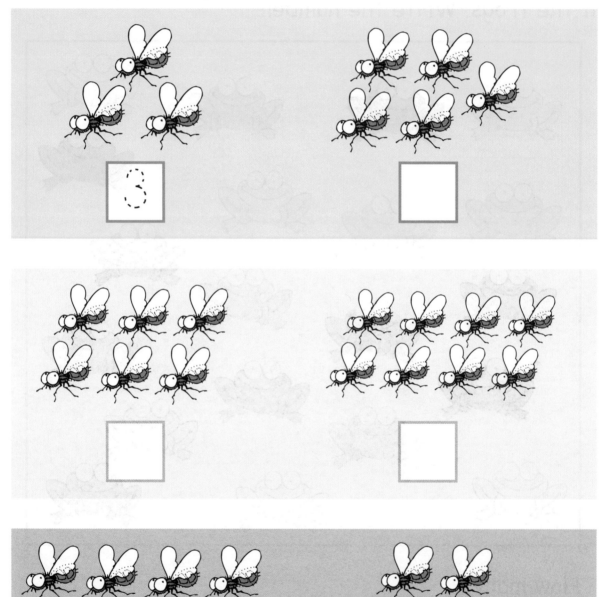

Super Skills for Summer • EMC 9830 • © Evan-Moor Corp.

Happy Birthday!

Color the presents.

Trace.

q q q q q

Candles

Count the candles in each box.
Circle the correct number in each box.

Super Skills for Summer • EMC 9830 • © Evan-Moor Corp.

What's in the Box?

Connect the dots.
Color the picture.

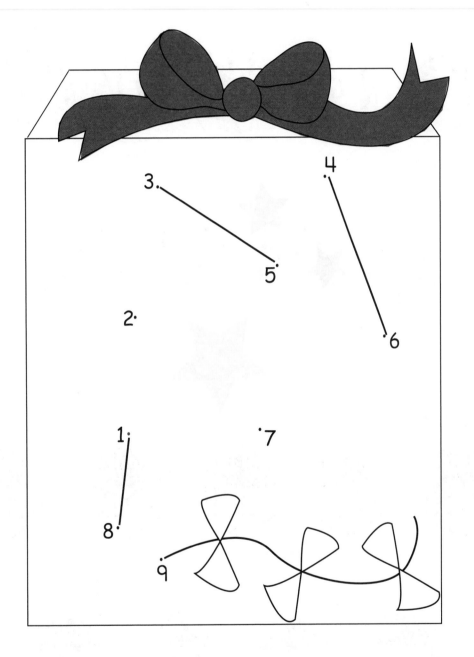

Let's Count

1 2 3 4 5 6 7 8 9

Trace the numbers.

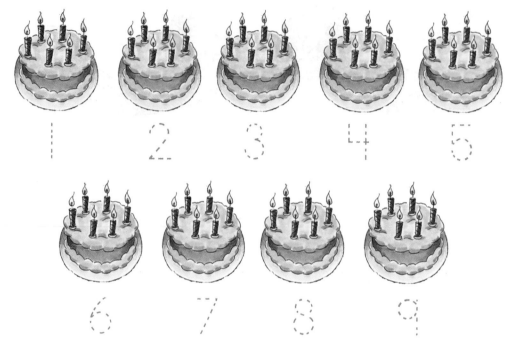

1   2   3   4   5

6   7   8   9

Write the numbers.

Super Skills for Summer • EMC 9830 • © Evan-Moor Corp.

Balloons

Color the balloons.

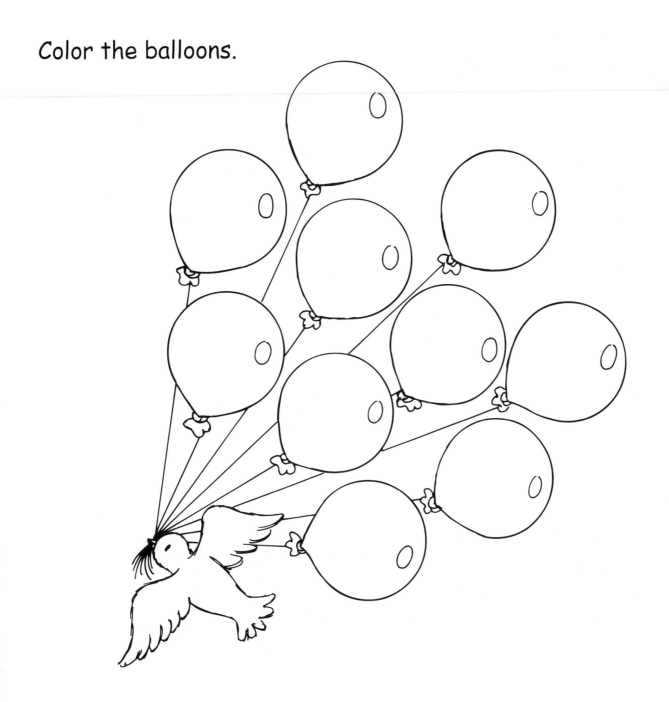

Trace.

10 10 10 10

How Many?

Count each set of balloons.
Circle the correct number.

4 5 6

6 7 8

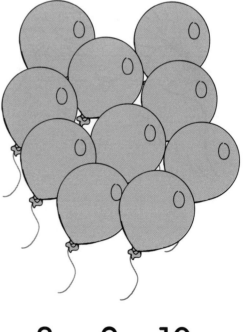

7 8 9

8 9 10

Super Skills for Summer • EMC 9830 • © Evan-Moor Corp.

1 2 3 4 5 6 7 8 9 10

Write the numbers.

• EMC 9830 • *Super Skills for Summer*   **213**

Up, Up, and Away

Connect the dots.
Color the balloon.

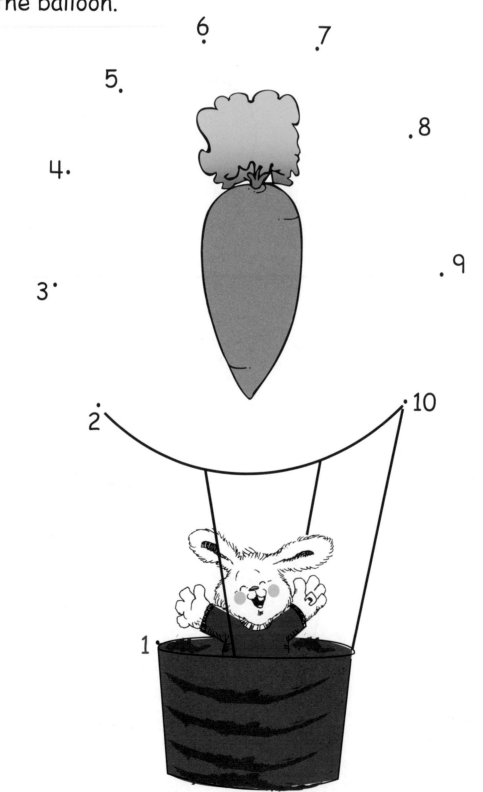

Super Skills for Summer • EMC 9830 • © Evan-Moor Corp.

Balloons for Sale

Make a match.

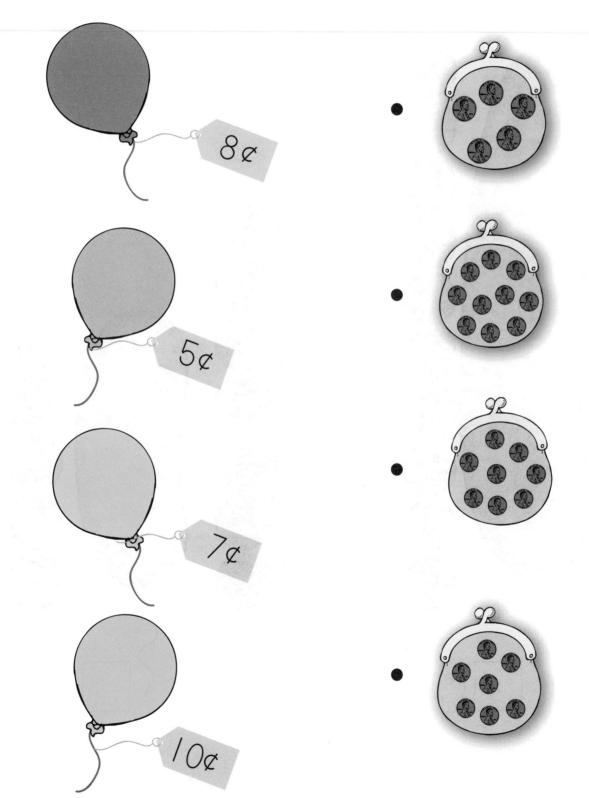

How Tall Is It?

How many pennies tall is each balloon?

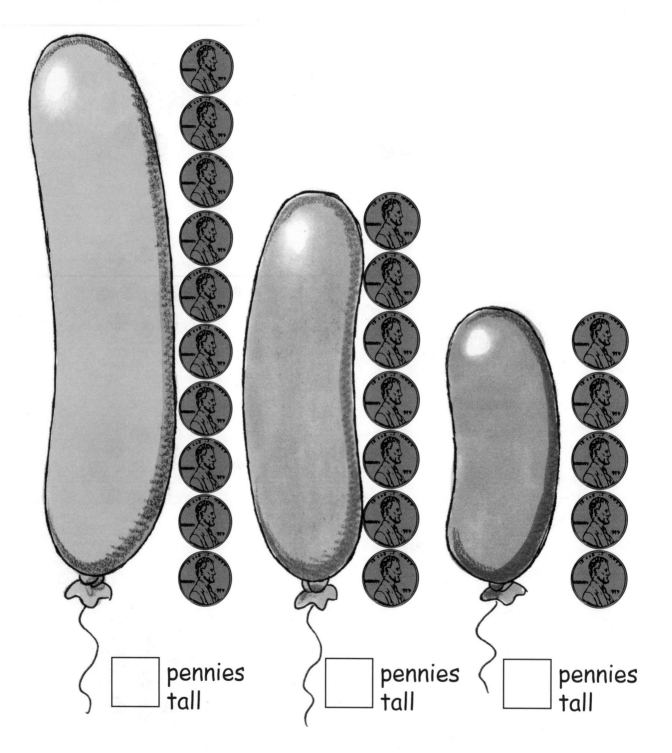

☐ pennies tall

☐ pennies tall

☐ pennies tall

Under the Sea

Trace the numbers.

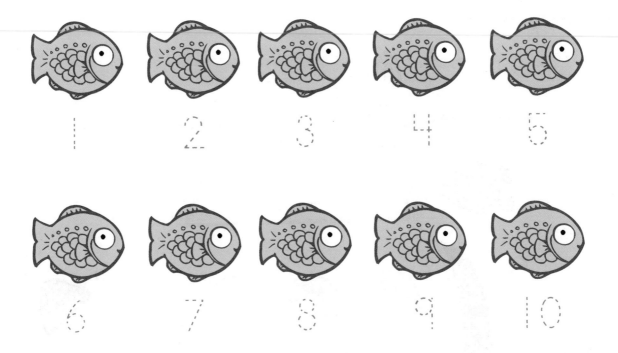

1   2   3   4   5

6   7   8   9   10

Write the numbers.

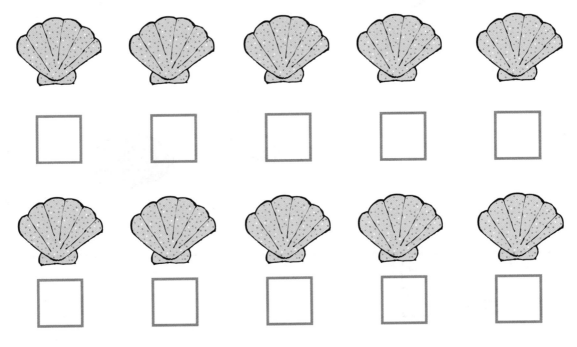

Down We Go

Connect the dots.
Color the picture.

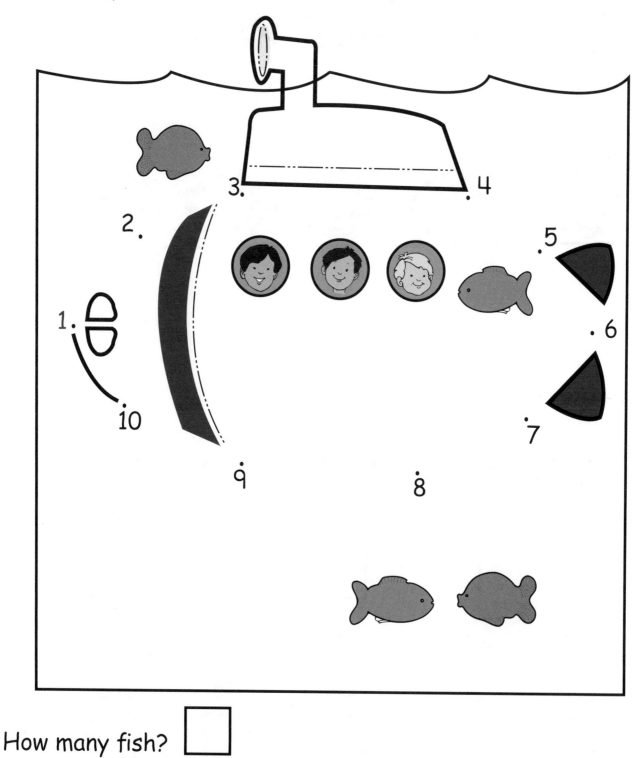

How many fish?

Super Skills for Summer • EMC 9830 • © Evan-Moor Corp.

Colorful Fish

Color the fish in each box.

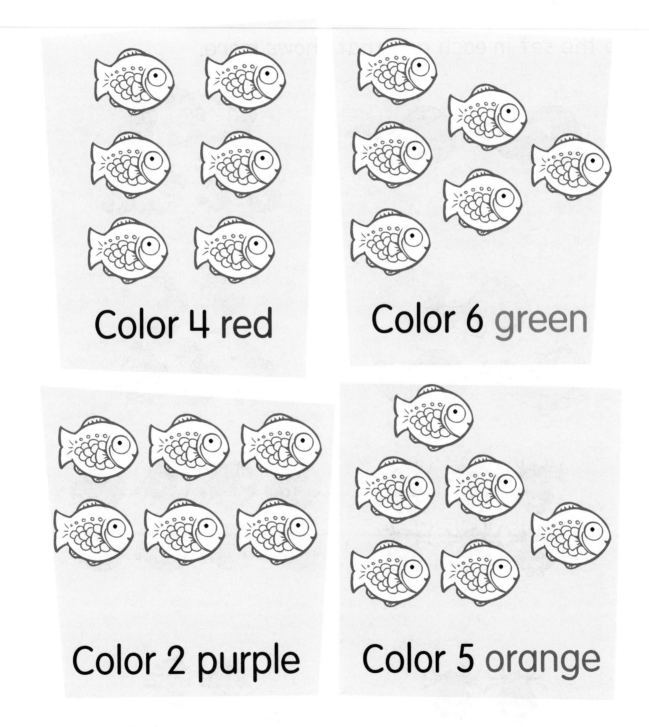

Color 4 red

Color 6 green

Color 2 purple

Color 5 orange

Which Is More?

1 2 3 4 5 6 7 8 9 10

Circle the set in each box that shows more.

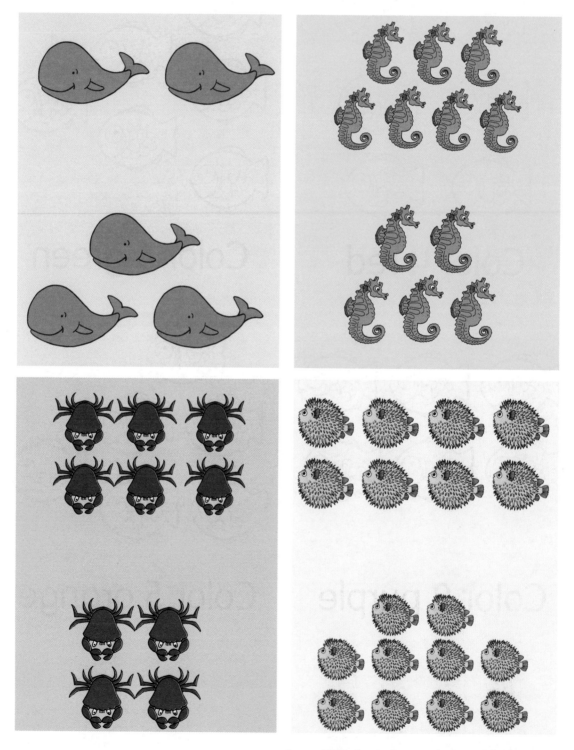

Super Skills for Summer • EMC 9830 • © Evan-Moor Corp.

Critical Thinking

Acorns and Leaves

Circle the picture that matches the first one in each row.

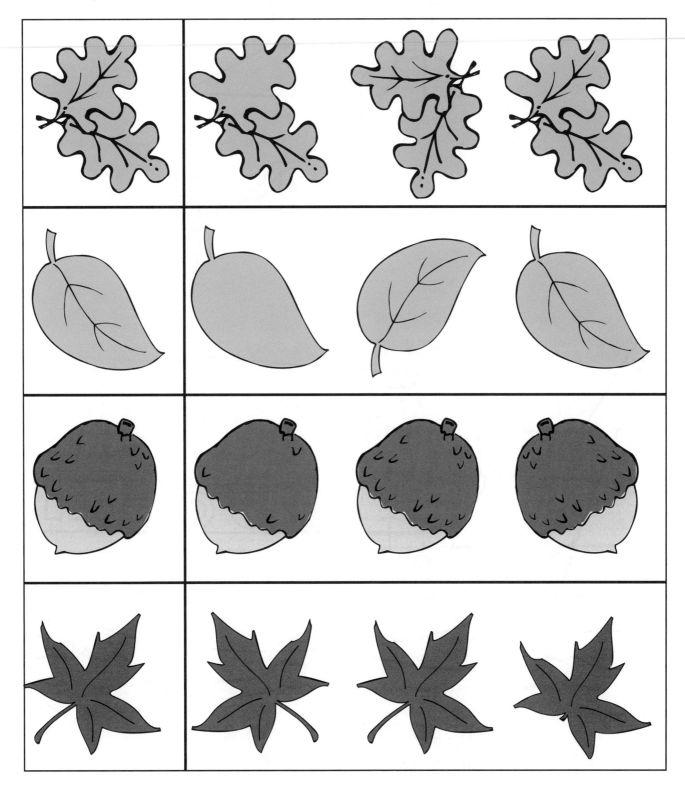

The Santa Maria

Color, cut, and glue
to finish the ship.

Columbus sailed to America.
His ship was named the *Santa Maria*.

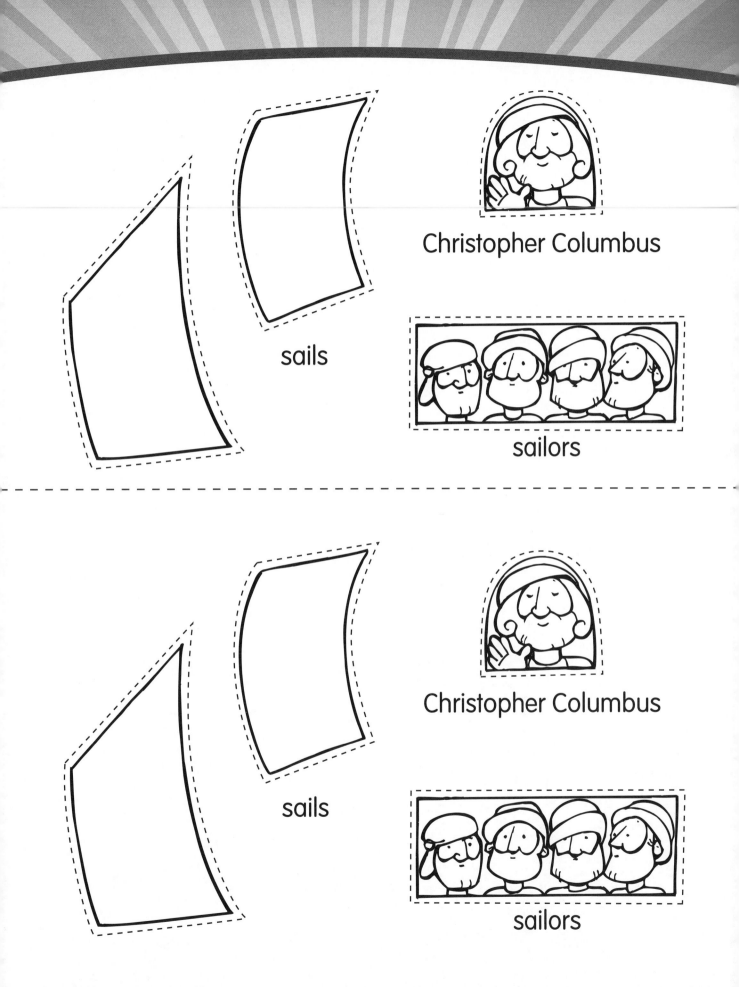

sails

Christopher Columbus

sailors

sails

Christopher Columbus

sailors

School Tools

Color the tools you
use at school.

It's Snowing!

Cut out the puzzle. Glue the pieces inside the frame.

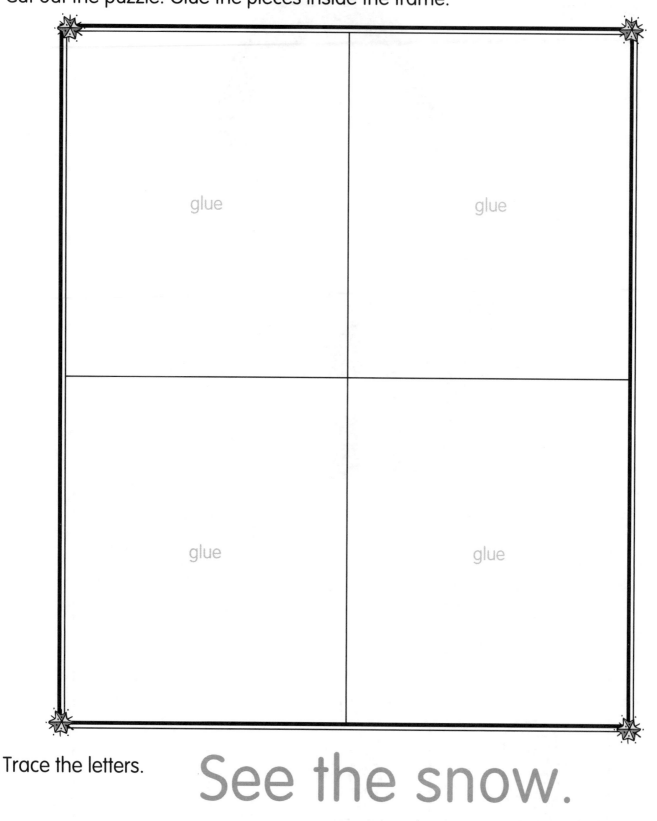

glue	glue
glue	glue

Trace the letters.

See the snow.

Note: Use this puzzle with the frame on page 228.

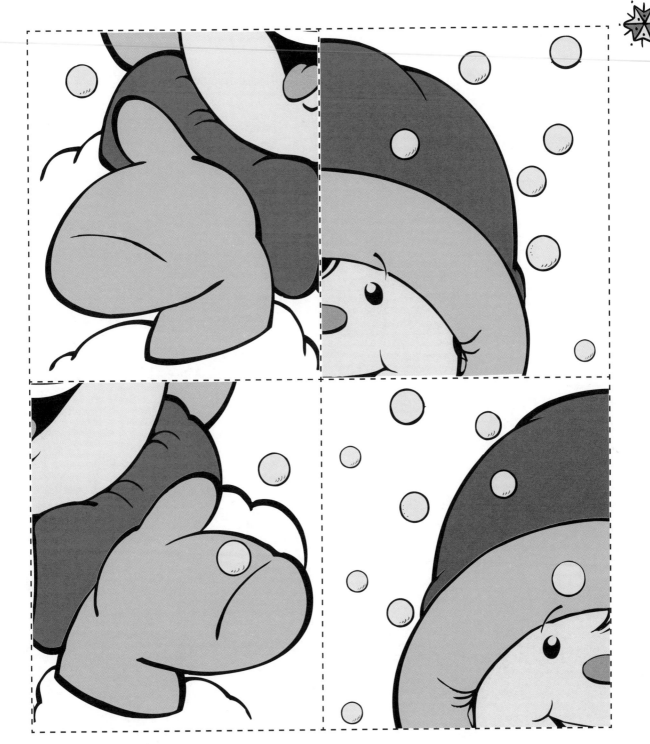

Kites

Make the kites the same in each row.

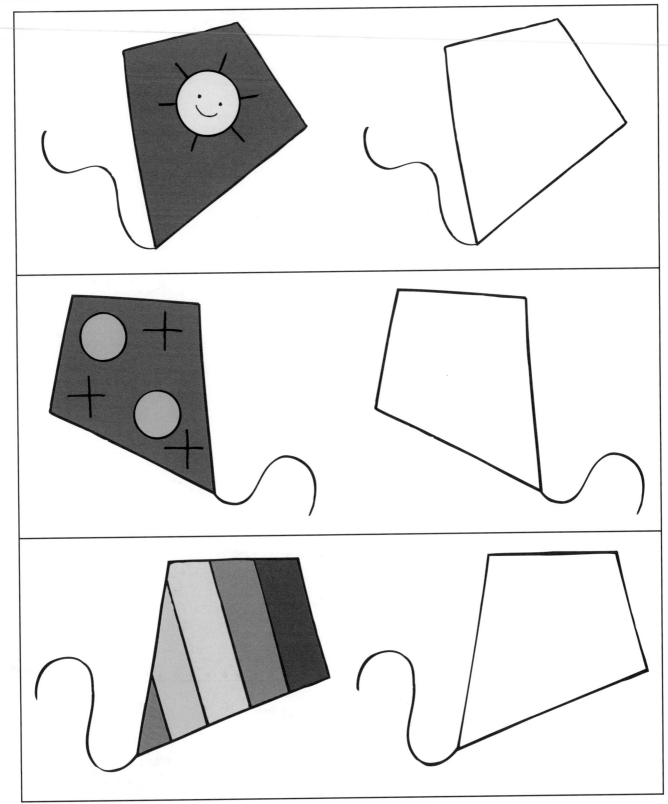

George Washington

Cut out the puzzle. Glue the pieces inside the frame.

Washington was the first president of the United States. George Washington's face is on the quarter.

Super Skills for Summer • EMC 9830 • © Evan-Moor Corp.

Note: Use this puzzle with the frame on page 232.

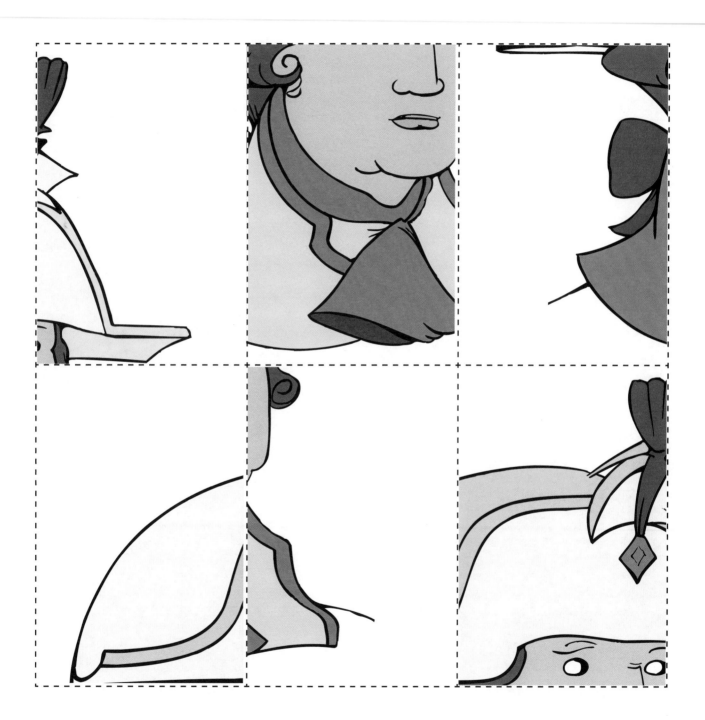

Draw Valentines

Make the second valentine like the first one.

Hearts

Find the hearts. Color them.

Circle how many you found.

1 2 3 4 5 6 7 8 9 10

March Winds

Cut out the missing pieces. Glue them in the picture.

The wind blows.

Seed to Flower

Cut out the pictures. Glue them in order.

glue	glue	glue

Mothers and Babies

Many babies are born in the spring. Draw a line to make a match.

Trace the letters.

The baby is little.

Lucky Shamrocks

shamrock

Find the shamrocks. Color them green.

How many shamrocks did you find?

1 2 3 4 5 6 7 8 9 10

Super Skills for Summer • EMC 9830 • © Evan-Moor Corp.

A Butterfly Grows

Cut out the pictures. Glue them in order.

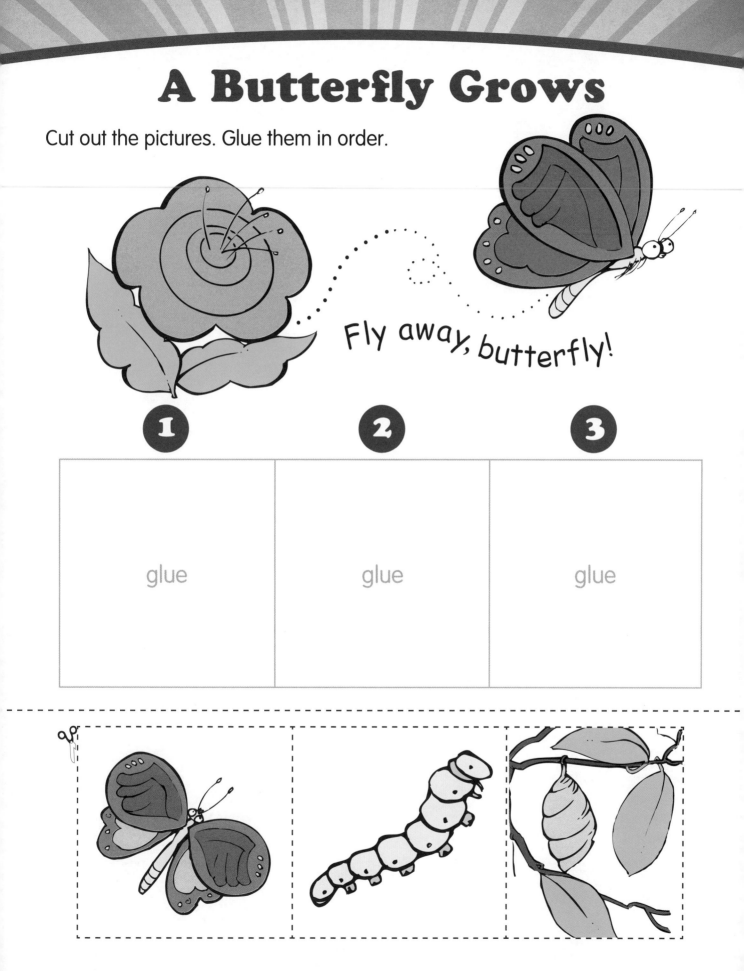

Fly away, butterfly!

1 **2** **3**

glue	glue	glue

Fiesta!

Draw a line to help the children get to the fiesta.

A fiesta is a party.
It is lots of fun.

May Day Surprise

Cut out the puzzle. Glue the pieces inside the frame.

glue   glue

glue   glue

Trace.   Happy May Day!

Super Skills for Summer • EMC 9830 • © Evan-Moor Corp.

In the Spring

Mother bird lays her eggs in the nest.

Glue the babies in the nest. Count the birds.

I see ___ birds.

Easter Fun

Circle the picture that is the same as the first one in each row.

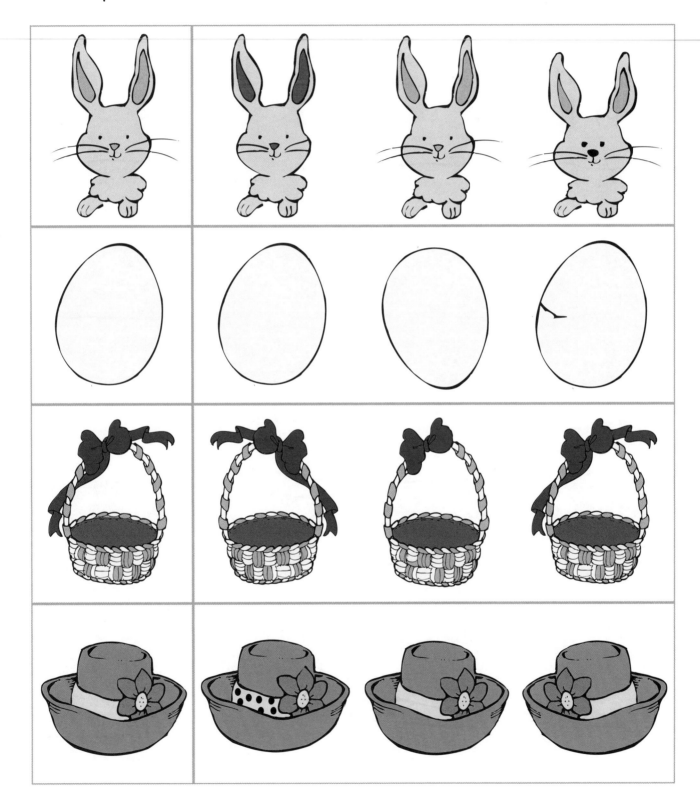

By the Sea

What fun
it will be
To play
by the sea.

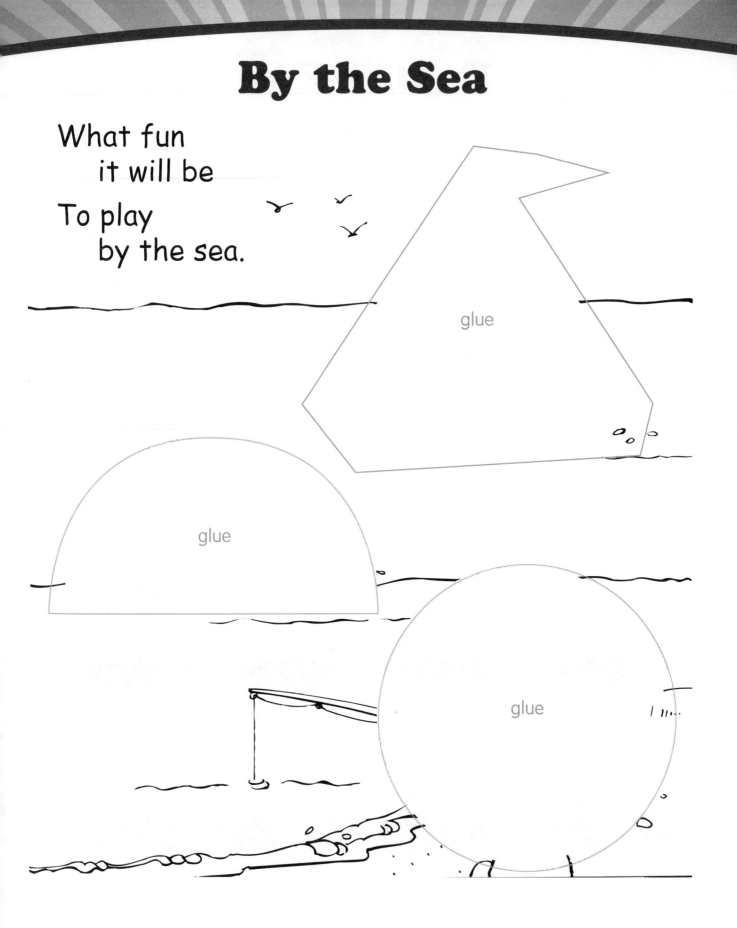

glue

glue

glue

Color. Cut. Glue onto page 252.

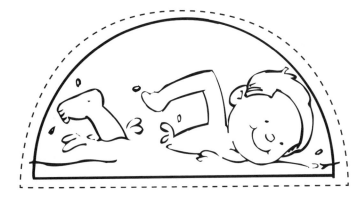

Answer Key

Page 147

Colors

Color the balloon **red**.

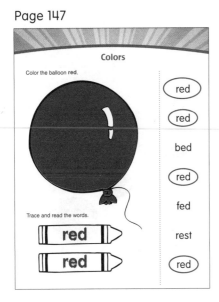

- (red)
- (red)
- bed
- (red)
- fed
- rest
- (red)

Trace and read the words.

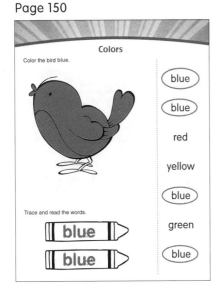 red

red

Page 148

Colors

Color the ● s green.

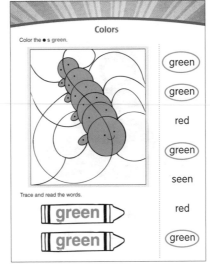

- (green)
- (green)
- red
- (green)
- seen
- red
- (green)

Trace and read the words.

green

green

Page 149

Colors

Color the ● s yellow.

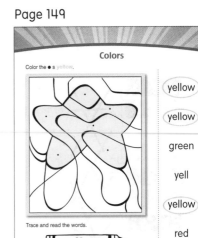

- (yellow)
- (yellow)
- green
- yell
- (yellow)
- red
- (yellow)

Trace and read the words.

yellow

yellow

Page 150

Colors

Color the bird blue.

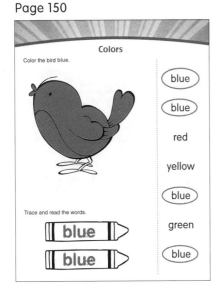

- (blue)
- (blue)
- red
- yellow
- (blue)
- green
- (blue)

Trace and read the words.

blue

blue

Page 151

Colors

Color the butterfly orange.

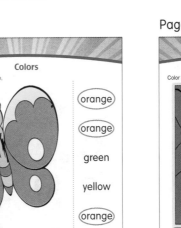

- (orange)
- (orange)
- green
- yellow
- (orange)
- green
- (orange)

Trace and read the words.

orange

orange

Page 152

Colors

Color the ● s **black**. Color the ■ s blue.

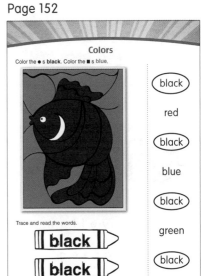

- black
- red
- (black)
- blue
- (black)
- green
- (black)

Trace and read the words.

black

black

Page 153

Colors

Color the ● s **brown**. Color the ■ s red.

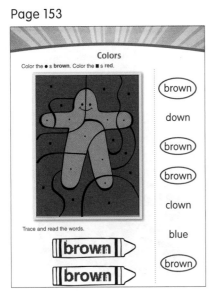

- (brown)
- down
- (brown)
- (brown)
- clown
- blue
- (brown)

Trace and read the words.

brown

brown

Page 154

Colors

Color the grapes **purple**.

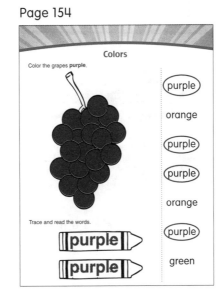

- (purple)
- orange
- (purple)
- (purple)
- orange
- (purple)
- green

Trace and read the words.

purple

purple

Page 155

Colors

Color the ● s blue. The clouds are white

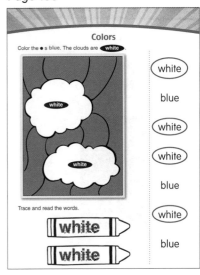

- white
- blue
- white
- white
- blue
- white
- blue

Trace and read the words.

white

white

Page 156

Colors

Draw lines to match each color.

- blue
- green
- black
- red
- white
- yellow
- purple
- orange
- brown

Page 157

Colors

Color the picture.

Write the color words.

The 🎀 (cape) is `r e d`.

The 🌿 (grass) is `g r e e n`.

Page 158

Colors

Trace the circles. Color them all.

Page 159

Colors

Color the picture.

Write the color words.

The 🐤 (chick) is `y e l l o w`.

The 🌿 (grass) is `g r e e n`.

Page 160

Colors

Color the shapes.

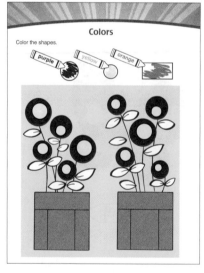

Page 161

Colors

Color the picture.

Write the color words.

The 🦇 (bat) is `b l a c k`.

The 🌙 (moon) is `y e l l o w`.

Page 162

Colors

Trace the shapes. Color the elephant.

Page 163

Colors

Color the picture.

Write the color words.

The 🐸 (frog) is `g r e e n`.

The 〰️ (water) is `b l u e`.

Page 164

Colors

Name the shapes. Color the shapes to match.

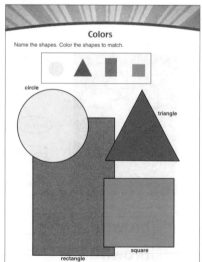

circle

triangle

rectangle

square

Super Skills for Summer • EMC 9830 • © Evan-Moor Corp.

Page 165

Colors

Color the picture.

Write the color words.

The 🥕 is o r a n g e.

The 🐢 is g r e e n.

Page 166

Colors

Trace the squares. Color them all.

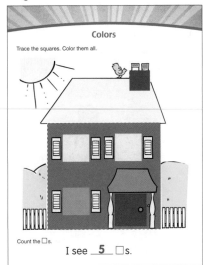

Count the ☐s.

I see __5__ ☐s.

Page 167

Colors

Color the picture. Make a blue coat on the bear.

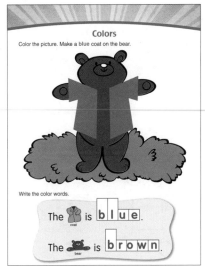

Write the color words.

The 🧥 is b l u e.

The 🐻 is b r o w n.

Page 168

Colors

Color the shapes.

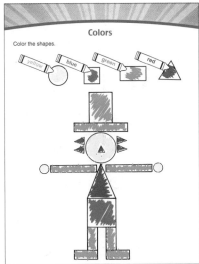

Page 171

1 Monkey

Color the monkey.

Colors may vary.

Trace.

| | | | | | |

Page 172

2 Bananas

Color the bananas.

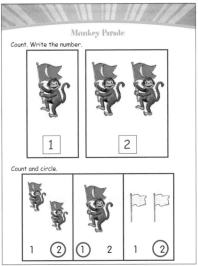

Trace.

2 2 2 2 2 2

Page 173

How Many?

Count. Circle the number.

Page 174

Monkey Parade

Count. Write the number.

Count and circle.

Page 175

Yummy Cookies

Color the cookies.

Colors may vary.

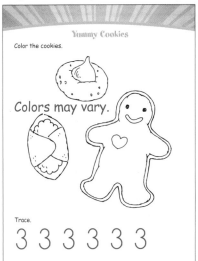

Trace.

3 3 3 3 3 3

Page 176

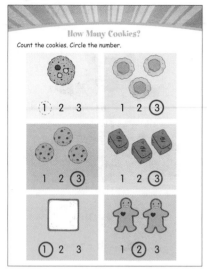

Page 177

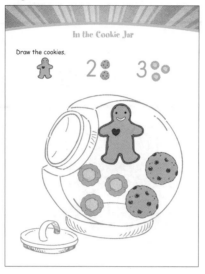

Page 178

Page 179

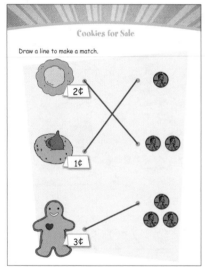

Page 180

Color will vary.

Page 181

Page 182

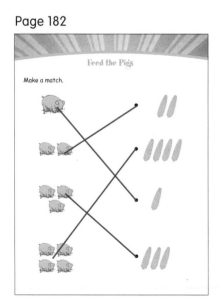

Page 183

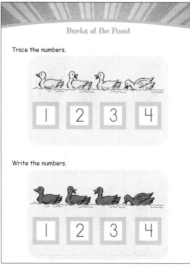

Page 184

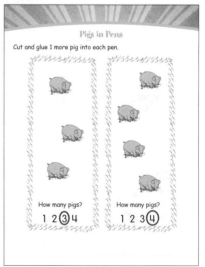

Page 185

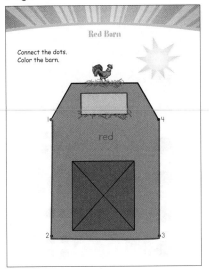

Red Barn

Connect the dots.
Color the barn.

red

Page 186

Pet Puppies

Color the puppies. Color will vary.

Trace.

5 5 5 5 5 5

Page 187

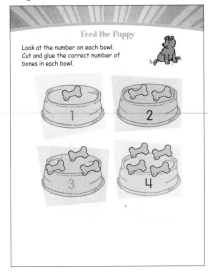

Feed the Puppy

Look at the number on each bowl.
Cut and glue the correct number of
bones in each bowl.

1   2
3   4

Page 188

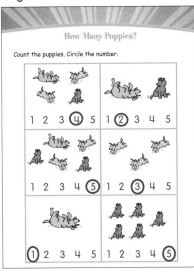

How Many Puppies?

Count the puppies. Circle the number.

1 2 3 ④ 5   1 ② 3 4 5
1 2 3 4 ⑤   1 2 ③ 4 5
① 2 3 4 5   1 2 3 4 ⑤

Page 190

Go Home, Puppy

Connect the dots.

Page 191

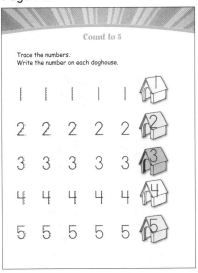

Count to 5

Trace the numbers.
Write the number on each doghouse.

| | | | |
2 2 2 2 2
3 3 3 3 3
4 4 4 4 4
5 5 5 5 5

Page 192

Hats for Sale

Color the hats. Colors will vary.

Trace.

6 6 6 6 6

Page 193

Fancy Hats

Look at the number in each box.
Draw the correct number of flowers on each hat.

2   4
6   3

Page 194

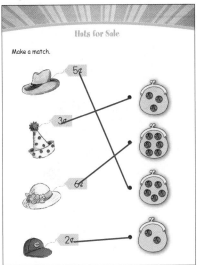

Hats for Sale

Make a match.

5¢
3¢
6¢
2¢

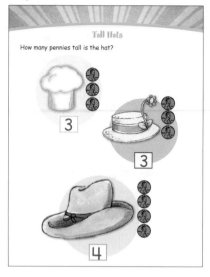

Tall Hats

How many pennies tall is the hat?

Ladybugs

Color the ladybugs.

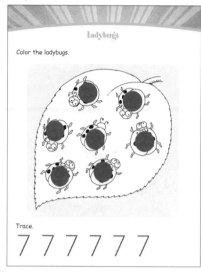

Trace.

7 7 7 7 7 7

Ladybug Babies

Draw a line from each ladybug to her baby or babies.

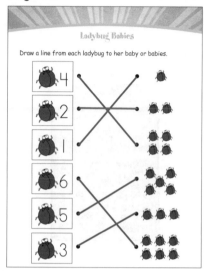

How Many?

Count the ladybugs in each box.
Circle the correct number in each box.

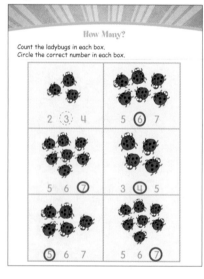

In the Jar

Look at the number below each jar.
Cut out the correct number of ladybugs
and glue them in each jar.

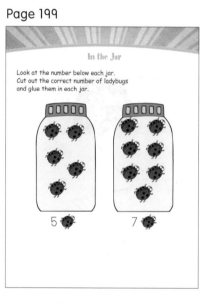

Where Are the Ladybugs?

Connect the dots. Color the picture.

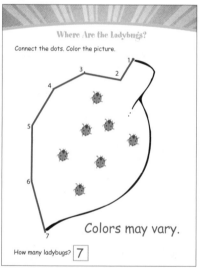

Colors may vary.

How many ladybugs? 7

In the Pond

Color the frogs.

Trace.

8 8 8 8 8 8

Hop to the Lily Pad

Draw a line. Match.

Finish the Frog

1 2 3 4 5 6 7 8

Connect the dots.
Color the frog green.

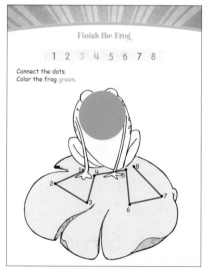

Page 205

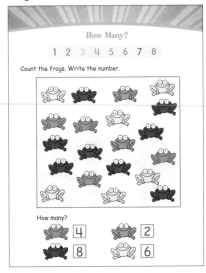

Page 206

Colors will vary.

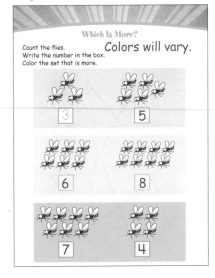

Page 207

Colors will vary.

Page 208

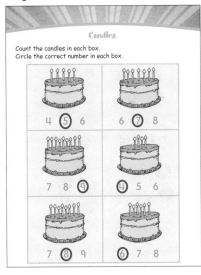

Page 209

Colors will vary.

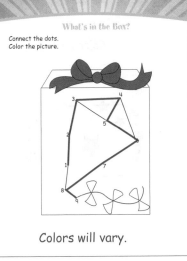

Page 210

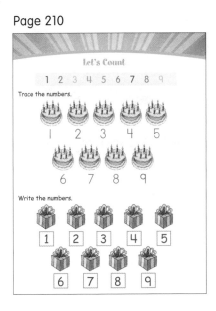

Page 211

Colors will vary.

Page 212

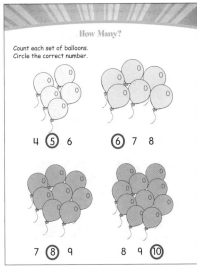

Page 213

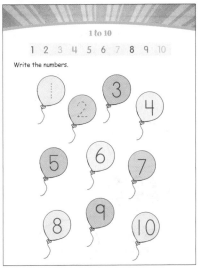

Page 214

Up, Up, and Away

Connect the dots.
Color the balloon.

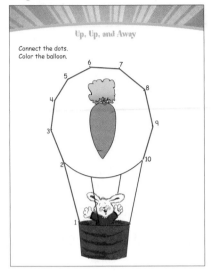

Page 215

Balloons for Sale

Make a match.

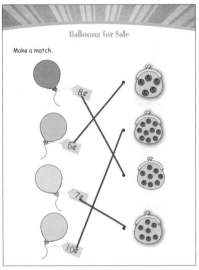

Page 216

How Tall Is It?

How many pennies tall is each balloon?

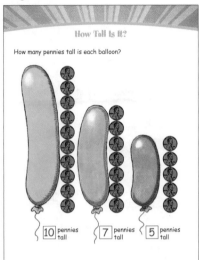

Page 217

Under the Sea

Trace the numbers.

1 2 3 4 5
6 7 8 9 10

Write the numbers.

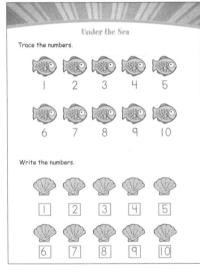

Page 218

Down We Go

Connect the dots.
Color the picture.

Colors will vary.

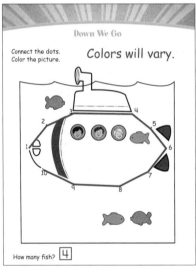

How many fish? 4

Page 219

Colorful Fish

Color the fish in each box.

Color 4 red   Color 6 green

Color 2 purple   Color 5 orange

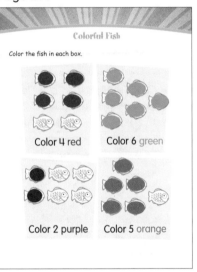

Page 220

Which Is More?

1 2 3 4 5 6 7 8 9 10

Circle the set in each box that shows more.

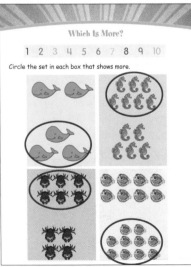

Page 221

Acorns and Leaves

Circle the picture that matches the first one in each row.

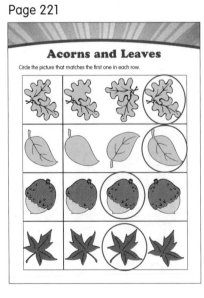

Page 224

The *Santa Maria*

Color, cut, and glue
to finish the ship.

Colors will vary.

Columbus sailed to America.
His ship was named the *Santa Maria*.

Page 225

School Tools

Color the tools you use at school.

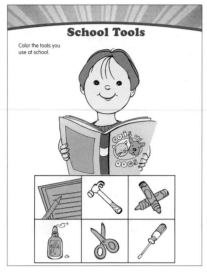

Page 228

It's Snowing!

Cut out the puzzle. Glue the pieces inside the frame.

Trace the letters.

See the snow.

Page 229

Kites

Make the kites the same in each row.

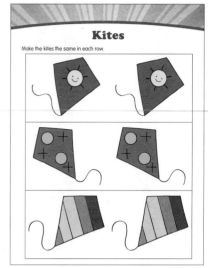

Page 232

George Washington

Cut out the puzzle. Glue the pieces inside the frame.

Washington was the first president of the United States. George Washington's face is on the quarter.

Page 233

Draw Valentines

Make the second valentine like the first one.

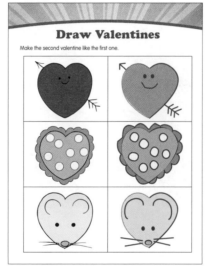

Page 236

Hearts

Find the hearts. Color them.

Circle how many you found.

1 2 3 4 5 6 7 8 9 (10)

Page 237

March Winds

Cut out the missing pieces. Glue them in the picture.

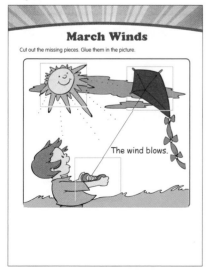

The wind blows.

Page 238

Seed to Flower

Cut out the pictures. Glue them in order.

Page 240

Mothers and Babies

Many babies are born in the spring. Draw a line to make a match.

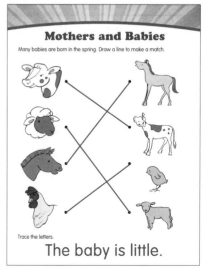

Trace the letters.

The baby is little.

Page 242

Lucky Shamrocks

Find the shamrocks. Color them green.

shamrock

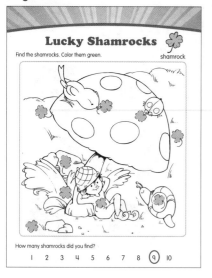

How many shamrocks did you find?

1 2 3 4 5 6 7 8 (9) 10

Page 243

A Butterfly Grows

Cut out the pictures. Glue them in order.

Fly away, butterfly!

1 2 3

Page 244

Fiesta!

Draw a line to help the children get to the fiesta.

A fiesta is a party.
It is lots of fun.

Page 246

May Day Surprise

Cut out the puzzle. Glue the pieces inside the frame.

Trace. Happy May Day!

Page 247

In the Spring

Mother bird lays her eggs in the nest.

Glue the babies in the nest. Count the birds.

nest

I see 3 birds.

Page 250

Easter Fun

Circle the picture that is the same as the first one in each row.

Page 252

By the Sea

What fun
it will be
To play
by the sea.

Colors will vary.